WOODCO

and

CHARCOAL BURNING

by

LYN ARMSTRONG

Published jointly by
COACH PUBLISHING HOUSE LTD
HORSHAM, SUSSEX
and
THE WEALD AND DOWNLAND OPEN AIR MUSEUM
SINGLETON, SUSSEX

Photoset and printed by
FLEXIPRINT LTD, ENGLAND

ISBN 0 905259 05 X

Frontispiece:
Charcoal Burners, c. 1890. Brushwood screens — tied in faggots shelter the kiln from wind. A charcoal burner's barrow forms a seat for one of the men. The wood to be charred is pointed at the ends so that it does not form a seal with the ground.

WOODCOLLIERS
and
CHARCOAL BURNING

by
Lyn Armstrong

Acknowledgements

The great heat generated, melted ore which formed
on hearth for forging and shaping

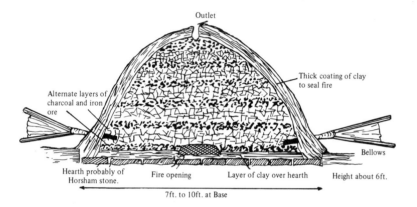

Outlet

Thick coating of clay
to seal fire

Alternate layers of
charcoal and iron
ore

Bellows

Hearth probably of
Horsham stone.

Fire opening

Layer of clay over hearth

Height about 6ft.

7ft. to 10ft. at Base

1.   Diagram of a bloomery

(By courtesy of Mr. F. Holmes)

DIAGRAMS

ACKNOWLEDGEMENTS

The author wishes to thank Mr. C. J. Bond of the Oxfordshire County Museum, who has very generously made available for quotation notes he has taken of early documentary material relating to charcoal burning for a work of his yet to be published, and for his account of the Wyre Forest burn.

To Mr. A. B. Bartlett, Archivist to the Beaulieu Estate, who gave permission to quote from an account he has drawn up of the ironworks at Sowley in the Beaulieu estate.

To Mr. F. G. Holmes of Horsham, Mr. A. W. Norris of Sparkbridge and Mr. J. Allonby of Sparkbridge for their diagrams and information, and in particular to Mr. and Mrs. A. Langridge of Kingsfold, Sussex, for their practical and advisory help during a number of years.

To Dr. H. Frost of London University, for the account he contributed on charcoal as a filter, given in the appendix.

Also to the several County Archivists and librarians who have assisted in finding relevant documents, to Major J. U. Machell for permission to quote from the Machell family records, and to the Bewdley Museum for giving access to papers held there on charcoal burning in the Wyre Forest.

The following acknowledgements are for the use of photographs:

The Mansell Collection
The Museum of English Rural Life, University of Reading.
The British Library.
Mr. J. R. M. Lyne.
Dr. P. Fordham.
J. Salmon Limited.
Mr. S. Hanna.
Mr. G. G. Garland.
BBC Hulton Picture Library.

Also to Messrs. King's Fuels of Edenbridge for their diagram of a metal kiln, and for the "working instructions" (page 84) and to Mr. D. W. Kelley of Messrs. Shirley Aldred & Co. Limited for helpful information.

PLATES

Cover. Charcoal burners in Epping Forest. c. 1879. (Mansell Collection).

Frontispiece. Charcoal kiln building. c. 1890. By permission of the Museum of English Rural Life, Reading.

1. Hut construction, setting up the poles. Weald & Downland Open Air Museum, Singleton, Sussex.
2. Hut construction, covering with sacks and turf.
3. The turf hut complete.
4. Bed inside the hut.
5. Huts, c. 1890; perhaps in the Slindon area (Sussex). Museum of English Rural Life, Reading.
6. Turf hut in the Wyre Forest. (Museum of English Rural Life).
7. Turf hut in Essex. (Photo. Hazeldine Warren, Museum of English Rural Life).
8. Bark peelers' hut, Cumbria.
9. Charcoal burners' hut, Ickenthwaite. (Photo. J. R. M. Lynne, 1972).
10. "Living hut", Statterthwaite. (Photo. S. Hanna, 1974).
11. Triangular flue commenced. Weald & Downland Museum.
12. Illustration to "Sylva" by John Evelyn.
13. Kiln with outer wood in place. Weald & Downland Museum.
14. Illustration of unknown origin, possibly 18th century and probably central European. (Radio Times, Hulton Picture Library).
15. Burning kiln in Kenya. (Photo. P. Fordham).
16. Core of long kiln in Kenya. (Photo. P. Fordham).
17. Engraving showing kiln building, probably 18th century. (Mansell Collection).
18. Engraving showing kiln building, probably 18th century. (Mansell Collection).
19. Flue at Blist Hill Museum, Coalbrookdale. (Photo. J. R. Armstrong).
20. Kiln at Gutach Open Air Museum, Black Forest. (Photo. J. R. Armstrong).
21. Kiln at Open Air Museum, Maria Saal, Austria. (Photo. J. R. Armstrong).
22. Detail of central flue of kiln at Maria Saal, Austria. (Photo. J. R. Armstrong).
23. A partly covered kiln, 1939, Petworth district, perhaps at Burton. (By permission of G. G. Garland).
24. A start to a central flue, Wyre Forest. (Mansell Collection).
25. Kiln with "motty-peg" flue, Statterthwaite. (Photo. S. Hanna).
26. The Ickenthwaite demonstration. (Photo. J. Salmon).
27. Charcoal burners lighting up, Forest of Dean. (Mansell Collection).
28. Dressing the stack, Weald & Downland Museum, 1972. (Photo. J. R. Armstrong).
29. Sealing the stack, Statterthwaite. (Photo. S. Hanna).
30. A smoking kiln, Weald & Downland Museum. (Photo. J. R. Armstrong).
31. A smoking kiln of the 1890s. (Museum of English Rural Life).
32. Charcoal burning in Kent, c. 1950. (Photo. J. R. Armstrong).
33. Charcoal burner raking the pit, Wyre Forest. (Mansell Collection).
34. An artist's impression of charcoal burning. (Radio Times, Hulton Picture Library).
35. Charcoal burners, Ambleside. (Radio Times, Hulton Picture Library).
36. Sorting charcoal at the Weald & Downland Museum. (Photo. J. R. Armstrong).
37. Using a rib shovel. (Photo. "Portsmouth News").
38. Charcoal burning, c. 1890, showing a curved ladder. (Museum of English Rural Life).
39. Two drawings of the retort at Faversham gunpowder factory.
40. Metal structure of central flue for metal kiln burning at the plant of the Sussex Charcoal Burning Company at Charlton, nr. Singleton, in 1938. (Coll. G. G. Garland).
41. Retaining cage being put around wood to be charred with smoking kilns in the background at Charlton. (Coll. G. G. Garland).
42. As above, removing the outer covering by pulley — it can then be slid along the scaffolding for use at another point. (Coll. G. G. Garland).
43. Metal kiln at Heyshott Common, 1970. (Photo. J. R. Armstrong).
44. Metal kilns at Heyshott Common, 1970. (Photo. J. R. Armstrong).
45. Kilns seen in Morocco, 1957. (Photo. J. R. Armstrong).
46. Charcoal burning in the Alps. (Mansell Collection).

INTRODUCTION:
THE HISTORICAL BACKGROUND

For about five thousand years — ever since metals were first smelted — it would seem that the production of charcoal by the controlled burning of wood with a restricted air supply under a cover of earth, or by splashing the burning wood with water, has been carried on. Travellers' photographs show some differences in the size and shape of kilns in Europe and elsewhere, and J. Morewood Dowsett, writing for the Geographical Magazine (January, 1946), tells us that in China charcoal is made in pits, preferably in a clay soil, and that in Sweden rectangular piles of wood are built up; but the method was much the same, and did not allow for great variation until, with the introduction of metal kilns, wood distillation plant and retort factories, it changed a great deal during the present century.

Before this it had been a dying craft; in October 1939, The Sussex County Magazine carried an article entitled "The Last Charcoal Burner", and Miss Dorothy Hartley, in her book "Made in England" published in 1939, wrote that she saw a charcoal burner at work in the woods of Kent at about that time. The present writer also remembers a charcoal burners' encampment in Kent in the late nineteen-thirties, but by then such a sight was unusual. These were burnings under the old fashioned earth covered kilns, although the metal kilns which have replaced them, were already coming into use.

"The Last Charcoal Burner", however, a Mr. Frank Harber, living at Plaistow, was not quite the last. Mr. James (Jim) Francis continued to make charcoal in earth kilns until 1948. His son-in-law, Mr. A. Langridge, learned the craft from him and worked with him. In 1968, The Weald and Downland Open Air Museum, at Singleton, was fortunate in making contact with Mr. and Mrs. Langridge (Mr. Francis' daughter), who most generously gave of their work and experience in re-constructing a camp on the Museum site and demonstrating charcoal burning on several occasions. They have been consulted frequently in the preparation of this booklet.

In Worcestershire, a retired charcoal burner, Mr. Potter, carried out a demonstration burn in 1956 and, in 1973, another burner, Mr. Nevey, carried out a reconstruction burn in conjunction with the Bewdley Museum and the Worcestershire County Museum. Unfortunately, neither Mr. Nevey, Mr. Potter, nor Mr. Booten — another Wyre Forest burner — are still alive. In Cumbria, Mr. Jack Allonby, whose family had been charcoal burners, set up two re-construction burns in the Furness Fells — at Ickenthwaite in 1972 and at Statterthwaite in 1974. Both of these demonstrations were filmed. Mr. Allonby, whose memories, like those of Mrs. Langridge, go back to the impressionable years of youth, and his friend, Mr. Norris, who helped with the Ickenthwaite burn, have supplied the information about the Cumbrian tradition for this account.

Charcoal is a carbon obtained by the controlled burning of wood with a restricted air supply. Coke is a mineral charcoal, but it is with wood charcoal that we are here concerned. In the charring process, water and volatile compounds are driven off and the residue of carbon has, when used as a fuel, the property of giving intense heat, about twice that of wood. Its composition, when prepared at a temperature of about 500°C., consists of carbon 30, hydrogen 10, oxygen with traces of nitrogen and sulphur.[1] It has a number of modern uses, some of which are listed in a later section.

Historically, as a fuel, its greatest importance was to the metallurgical industries, and in particular to the manufacture of iron and steel. In England, there is evidence of iron working before the Roman occupation — in the Severn Valley, the Forest of Dean and to some extent at least in the south and south-east, at Pipers Close, near Kirdford, and between Hastings, Battle and Tunbridge Wells. With the coming of the Romans the industry expanded and large quantities of furnace slag used by them as hardcore in roadmaking have been found. The large mounds, about fifty feet high, of this slag which stood at Beauport Park, near Battle, were demolished in the 19th Century.[2]

Following the Roman occupation there is as yet no archaeological evidence that iron-smelting continued to be practised, and it has been surmised that all Saxon iron work must have been imported: this seems improbable. A reference in Doomsday Survey to iron working in the Hundred of East Grinstead in Sussex suggests that the industry, if very much diminished, did actually survive.

[3]In 1217, the Forest Charter laid a charge of 2d. per year per cart and ½d. per year per pack horse for wood and charcoal removed from the royal forests. This was an attempt to control woodland exploitation — it would also be a source of revenue.[3a]

In the Forest of Dean, between Michaelmas 1278, and April 1279, licences to burn charcoal were sold to fifty-three different men for a total of £101.5.6d. at prices ranging from £6.11s. for twenty-three continuous weeks down to 6s. for a fortnight.[3b]

Court cases were brought for the infringement of forest restrictions; for instance, the Forest Pleas of Wychwood record that in 1272 John de Wyke of Ditchley and five others were convicted and detained in prison for being habitual offenders in respect of the vert and charcoal burners in the Forest without warrant. Hugh and Richard, charcoal burners of Ditchley, were also imprisoned as "habitual poachers of the King's deer".[3c]

In 1255-6, several convictions are recorded for charcoal burning without a licence in Needwood Forest, Staffs, and in 1498 in Epping Forest, Thomas Parker, was accused of "destroying the King's vert in the making of coals and selling them by the sack to the great destruction of all the covert".[3d]

In 1290, the export of charcoal was actually prohibited from the Weald of Sussex and Kent.[3e]

In Cumbria, the Cistercians of Furness Abbey organized their woodlands for production. Their tenants had "livery iron" and the rights to some wood for charcoaling, their licences being clearly defined and fines levied for infringements.

Increasingly the smelting of iron and iron working prospered. Until the fifteenth century, iron was produced by burning the crushed ore between layers of charcoal in a bloomery, a mound-shaped construction over a stone hearth, covered by a layer of clay. Mr. Frank Holmes, of Horsham, has given permission to reproduce a drawing he made giving an impression of such a bloomery. (Fig. 1).

The bellows provided a sufficient draught through the heap to the outlet at the top. A bloomery could be used only once, the clay crust being broken open, although the hearth could be used repeatedly. The iron produced was softened but not liquid and was beaten free of cinder. The resulting bloom of iron was then suitable for use as "wrought" iron; "cast" iron was not produced by this method, nor at that time desired; if by accident the heat became greater than that necessary for wrought iron smelting, and the metal liquified, it became waste.[4]

In the late fifteenth century, when the possibility had been realised of casting cannon in one piece instead of the earlier culverins and mortars which were made of separate pieces of iron banded together, the use of furnaces capable of producing the large quantities of molten iron needed to fill the cannon moulds was introduced into the Weald from the Ardennes, where they seem to have been in existence for some time.[5] These "blast" furnaces, as they came to be called, were built with protective walls and a wide chimney or open top and fitted with large and powerful bellows working in pairs compressed by a rotating wheel driven by water or animal power. Work could be carried on, feeding in through the top layers of charcoal and ore, continuously. The molten iron was run off into moulds at the base and the cinder drawn off through vents: the fire could be kept alive for long periods of time. The proportion of charcoal used seems to have been one load to a load of ore — and additional charcoal was required for a preliminary treatment of the "mine" (i.e. ore) to break it up and prepare it for the furnace.

More and more cannon were required, cannon balls also. England had iron ore and the timber for fuel, and by the time of Queen Elizabeth, for a few years had a monopoly for the export of iron cannon.

Wrought iron was, of course, also needed: horse shoes, implements and tools, nails and domestic items such as hinges had to be supplied. There were set-backs; the Black Death struck twice within the fourteenth century, but the iron industry regained its importance and continued to expand. By the sixteenth century charcoal was demanded in enormous quantities. In 1547 the iron works at Worth, in Sussex, recorded the consumption during the two previous years of nearly 6,000 cords of wood for the furnace and 3,000 for the forge. A thriving glass industry also required charcoal, and in addition much was used — particularly in London — as domestic fuel. Wood for implement making and for manufacture, the building of houses and for ship building added to the demand for timber so that the devastation of the great forests became a cause for concern. In the sixteenth century, Acts of Parliament were passed with the purpose of safeguarding the maintenance of the woodlands.

In 1565 it was found necessary, temporarily, to suppress all the bloomeries in Furness in order that woods might not be further destroyed.[6] A Royal Commission, set up in 1573, reported of the Wealden area: "Besides these furnaces aforesaid, there are not so few as a hundred furnaces and Iron Mylles in Sussex, Surrey and Kent, which is greatly to the decaie, spoile and overthrowe of woods and principle tymber, with a great decaye also of tillage for that they are continuallie employed in carrying of furniture for the said workes, and likewise a great decaie of the highways because they carrie all the wyntertyme". Regulations were made prohibiting the making of charcoal from mature wood — coppice must be used. The use of wood for charring was prohibited within eighteen miles of London or eight from the Thames, the cutting of timber was restricted within twelve miles of the coast. In 1574 the Privy Council obliged all makers of cannon to enter into bonds not to manufacture iron within fourteen miles of the Thames. No new iron works were to be erected within twenty-two miles of London. The central Weald prospered under these conditions and the struggle for supplies went on. John Norden, in his "Surveyor's Dialogue" of 1607 wrote: "He that observes it, and hath known the Weald of Surrey, Sussex and Kent, the grand nursery of oak and beech, shall find an alteration within less than thirty years as may well strike fear lest few years more as pestilent as the former will leave few good trees standing in those wealds". It can be argued that to some extent the "complaints" had political motives and that as tension developed with Spain, there was fear that the

English export industry might be directing cannon into Spanish hands. The interests competing for the timber supply were emphatic that livelihoods were threatened and quick to point out that the cost of iron itself had escalated. The price of charcoal was, on an annual reckoning, the iron industry's highest cost.

The complaints of the time are poetically expressed by Michael Drayton in his "Polybion" (1607), where he describes the Nymphs fleeing to the Downs to escape the noisy horror of the iron works and the trees being felled, while the "Sylvans", native countrymen, are driven to wander "far abroad" as the source of their livelihood was carried away in timber carts. Speaking in the voice of the trees he laments:

> "Jove's oak, the warlike ashe, vein'd elm, the softer beech,
> Short hazel, maple plain, light apse, the bending wych,
> Tough holly and smooth birch must altogether burn,
> What should the builder save, supplies the forger's turn,
> When under public good, base private gain takes hold,
> And we, poor woeful woods, to ruin lastly sold."

(The ash, "warlike" had in earlier times been valued for spear shafts.)

After the dispersal of the Armada in 1588, an Order in Council sent a letter to Lord Howard of Effingham instructing him to appoint a "discreet gentleman" to visit the foundries and stop the casting of guns. This prohibition, if ever it became enforced, did not last long. During the period from the death of Elizabeth I to the Civil War, the demand for guns was not great, but with the outbreak of the civil war, complications ensued which caused great damage to the trade. Royalist-owned iron works were blown up and destroyed. The forests of Royalists which had been sequestered were sold by the Government to raise funds — or, alternatively, sold by their owners to pay fines.[7] Perhaps because the Paliamentarians feared the proximity of the south-east to the Continent, its significance as an escape route and source of possible aid to the Stuart cause, the Wealden iron industry suffered greatly although those works whose owners were favourable to the Parliamentary party flourished. The shortage of timber, however, was felt not only there, but wherever the making of wood charcoal had depleted the forests, for iron making or for other purposes.

The Lancashire County Records Office[8] holds the papers relating to a dispute between the owners of two iron works who had entered into articles to buy wood and charcoal jointly, thus avoiding competitive pricing. The grounds for the dispute were that one of the partners had cut and used wood from his own coppice without throwing it into the mutual supply. The coppice was estimated to make 1,000 dozen sacks of coal. The other party was countercharged with having obtained a consignment of coals after the date when the agreement was drawn up — but before it was signed — and of having used them for some length of time. Representations made by both parties kept a vigorous lawsuit active for twelve years between 1714 and 1726.

Experiments had been carried out from the beginning of the seventeenth century to convert or "charke" pit-coal (called sea-cole because it was carried by boat) but it was only after 1735, when Abraham Darby succeeded in making a satisfactory coke, that a new and plentiful fuel for smelting became available. The iron industry profited further with the harnessing of steam power — blast furnaces far more powerful than those previously designed were built and the coal fields, particularly when a good supply of water was also accessible, became the focal point for new development. After steam, came easy transport, while coal and coke became for most purposes the desirable fuel and the importance of the charcoal industry was certainly over. In Sussex, the charcoal fuelled furnace at Lamberhurst continued to work until 1811 and that at Backbarrow in Lancashire is believed to have been the last, bringing the practice into the present century.

Despite the depredations of the colliers, it is arguable that the need for timber on so great a scale actually preserved much woodland which might otherwise have been completely cleared in the opening out of more land for agriculture. The Royal Forests were always protected and as increasingly timber became a valuable crop, it was grown as such. From an early period, coppicing was practised on the better-managed estates, a system by which within fifteen years (or only twelve for hazel) such trees as oak, beech, ash and later, after it had become a common tree, sweet chestnut, could be brought to sufficient size grown from the boles of previously felled trees. With an assured market, this cycle, although longer, certainly than that for other crops, was well worth waiting for. Farm animals were excluded from coppices by the digging of ditches and setting up of hedges of quickthorn grown on banks. In the sixteenth century further regulations ordained that a dozen standard trees should be left to the acre after clear felling so that regeneration through seed might follow.

Sussex itself, though no longer covered by the great Andreadsweald Forest, is still the most wooded county in England. The forests in the west of Scotland did not survive, but the woodlands north of Furness, where the growth of coppice as a crop had been extensively carried on, although heavily drawn on for charcoal making (it is said that when the first Backbarrow furnace was set up in 1712, it consumed four years' local supply of charcoal in eight months) were not so destroyed; and they remain as a feature of the beautiful landscape except where farm clearance or modern forestry has required the land.

THE CHARCOAL-BURNING LIFE

On the Rufus stone, in the New Forest, is an inscription telling that a charcoal burner named Purkess conveyed the body of William II, killed while hunting and abandoned by his retinue, to Winchester for burial. The stone itself was erected towards the end of the eighteenth century and the historian, Sir Francis Palgrave, Deputy Keeper of Her Majesty's Records 1836-1861, who in his day had a high reputation, said in his "History of Normandy and of England" that the body of William was "saved from crow, dog and vermin only by the piety of a neighbouring charcoal burner, Purkis, who took compassion on the body and conveyed the remains from the solitude where the mortal wound was received . . . His family still subsists in the neighbourhood, nor have they risen above their original station, poor craftsmen or cottagers. They followed the calling of coal-burners until a recent period and they tell us that the wheel of the Cart that conveyed the neglected Corpse was shown by them until the last century".

Some of Palgrave's learned contemporaries, however, thought him "prone not to carry conviction to a sceptical temperament" and Edward Freeman[1] says that he "Had often heard of this legendary Purkis, but really, so palpable a fiction ought not to have found its way into the pages of a scholar like Sir Francis Palgrave . . . If anyone chooses to say that the cart was driven by Godwine or Aethelstan, we cannot say that it was not". Palgrave gives no reference for his account; the chronicles — themselves of a later date by some decades, but written well within living memory of the event — name no individual as bearer of the corpse; William of Malmsbury says it was taken by a few rustics in a cart and another account says that it was taken there by some inferior members of the dead king's entourage.

"It is estimated that in 1282 there were nine hundred charcoal burners working in the Forest of Dean in four of the King's demesne woods alone. In the fourteenth century those employed directly by the King were paid 3d. per day. They seem, like the miners, to have been for the most part free men working outside the manorial system. Sometimes they had alternative employment — a certain John Carbonarius held a cothold for a rent of 2/- cash, a caule of charcoal and three days service each of haymaking, harvesting and weeding on the prior of Worcester's demesne. Some charcoal burners named in the Forest of Dean, in the thirteenth century, had forges in the forest also. The charcoal burner appears to have marketed his crop himself, although a middleman is involved in a dispute at Cleobury Forge in the early seventeenth century."[2]

The notion of the "traditional" charcoal burner living in his hut from the time of the Conquest (or just after) until today has a romantic appeal, but one should guard against making a certainty of this. One fact which does emerge is that the Purkis family and the Tinsley family were, in later centuries, known as charcoal burners in the New Forest area, and a Will, preserved in the Hampshire Record Office,[3] made by a John Purkis in 1672 describes him as a collier. By Palgrave's time, if there were still charcoal burners of that name, he does not seem to have traced them and although the present telephone directory for the area includes a number of Purkis entries — and more must be living in the district — they are not "collyers".

This Will is of interest in the light it throws on the status of a collier of the seventeenth century and, as a contemporary document, worth quoting in full:

> In the name of God Amen the twentyeth day of October in the year of our Lord Christ one thousand six hundred and seventy two (English account). I John Purkiss the eldest of the parish of Minstead in the county of Southampton, Collyer, being sick and weake in bodye but of sound and perfect Memory praise be therefore given to Almighty god do make and ordayn this my last will and Testament in manner and form following (viz.). First and principally I command my soul unto the hand of almighty God hoping through the merritts death and passion of my saviour Jesus Christ to have full and free pardon and forgiveness for all my sins and to inherit everlasting life. And my body I commit to the earth to be decently buried at the discretion of my executor hereafter named and as touching the disposition of such temporal effects as it hath pleased God almighty to bestow upon me I give and dispose thereof as followeth; First I will that all my debts and funeral charges shall be payed and discharged; Also I doo give and bequeath unto my son John Purkiss my house and land in the Parish of Minstead called by the names of Longhoe and Newlands with the appurtances to the same of right aperteyning and belonging upon condition that he doo pay and clear of the morgage from Mistress Mary Crandon widdow, and also that my son John Purkiss doo permit my wife peaceably and quietly to enjoy her third of the aforesaid house and lands during her natural life. Item, I give to my daughter Mary Woolfe one shilling, and Item I give to my daughter Katherine Stryde one shilling. Item I give to my son William Purkiss one shilling. Item I give unto my son in law Richard Waldron one shilling. Item I give to my Daughter-in-law Dorothy Waldron one shilling. Item I give to my daughter Elizabeth Wright one shilling. Item I give to Elizabeth My wife, during her life, Crowchers ground with all the appurtance which do belong to the said lease and after the decease of the said Elizabeth Purkiss my wife the said lease of Crowchers lande to go unto my son William Purkiss if that my wife and executor be not forced to sell it to pay my debts; Item I will that Elizabeth my wife enjoys the Little Close

adjoining to my copyshold which is parcel of Rangers land during her natural life and after her decease (to goe) unto my son John Purkiss. Item I give to Thomas Grant and Clement Morris half a crown unto each of them desiring them to be the overseers of this my last will and testament hereby revoking, disannuling, and making void all former wills and testaments heretofore by me made whether by word or writing declared or menconed.

In witness hereof the day and year first above written I have hereunto set me hand and seal, 1672.

Acknowledged by John Purkiss the eldest to be his last will and testament before the witnesses,

Signed (etc.)

From this two points emerge: that John Purkiss, styling himself a collier by trade, owned his house and that he was not illiterate.

Other colliers' wills dating from the sixteenth to the eighteenth centuries reveal conditions dissimilar to those of Palgrave's "poor craftsmen and cottagers".

[4]John Wright of Epping, collier, who made his will in April 1568 must have been a relatively wealthy man. After the preamble and request that his body should be buried in Epping Churchyard, he makes the following bequests:

Item: I give unto the poormans box of the same parrishe, 5/-.
Item: I will that yf I do not fortune with my owne hande to distribute (being on my death bedd) 5/- unto the poor folkes, then that yt be unto them distributed as sone as I ame departed at the dyscression of my overseer and executrix.
Item: I will that Thomas my sonne shall have my money which Frances Benton oweth me, which is the whole somme of threescore and tyrtene pounds 13/4 of lawfull monye of Englande as it may appere by two severall obligations, in such manner as I ought to have them (and all thinges therin conteyned) yf I were lyvnge to have and enjoy the same.
Item: I will that my Executrix shall paye and delyver unto Thomas my sayde sonne so muche more of leafull monye as shall make up this former somme foure score poundes. All of which somme of monye I will that my said sonne shall receave and have at the age of 22 yeres. If my said sonne happen to dye before he accomplishes that age of 22 yeres, then I will that the said somme of foure score poundes remayne to onne Margery Mather and to Alys my wife equally to be devided. And if the saide Margery dye before she accomplishes the full age of 22 yeres, so that my sayd sonn be disceased also; then I will that her parte of the said somme shall remayne to the children of John Gouge of Roydon, equallye to be unto them devided.

Item: I will that Alys my wyfe or her assigner shall fynde and keepe my saide sonn Thomas at the scole untyll he have obteyned perfect knowledge of the Laten tongue.

Item: I will that yf Alys my saide wiefe shall happen to marrye that my overseer shall see her husbande put in or fynde sufficient sureties for the paiement and performaince of all my forsaid legacies in due maid.

All the rest of my goodes and chattelles not bequested (my debts and legacies paide) I give unto Alys my seide wyfe whom I make my sole Executrix of this my last will and testament.

Item: I ordeyne and make John Benton the elder of Eppinge aforesaide, my overseer of this my last will (to whom I will gyeve for his paynes 5/s.) to see the same performed in due meanes . . .

Unfortunately we have not the inventory for John Wright's estate.

John Rooke of Barking (1557)[5] and John Cordell of Cheshunt (1579)[5] left wills including cattle, farm and household goods; the will of John Fuller[5] of Northweald (1601) includes the "tooles and implements belonging to my trade of coalinge" with other bequests of unspecified goods and chattels to his wife, but mentioning some domestic furnishings:

"Item; I will that my table now standing in the hall of my house with one bench and one form thereto now belongynge, and also my standinge bedsteede in my chamber and one fetherbedd and boulster, two pillows, one blankett and one coverlett to the said beddstedel now belonginge are hereupon lying shall stand contynue and remaine in and unto my house aforesaid as may they doo without takeinge awaie and displacenge unto those whom I have appointed my said house after the decease of my wife."

This will carries the testator's mark, not his signature. Unfortunately none of the wills coming from Kent, Sussex, Hampshire or Essex can be certainly ascribed to colliers working for the iron masters, and they tell us very little about the trade. Inventories, required by law from the time of Henry VIII for probate — from the same counties — have the same limitation, but are interesting in that they give some idea of the way of life of a few individuals and of money values then obtaining.

The inventory of the goods of Thomas Alderton, a collier of Northchapel in the county of Sussex, dated 1647, reveals that his house — which he did not own — had a hall, his chamber, a room over his chamber, a hall chamber, a buttery and a kitchen in which possessions stood as follows:[6]

Imprimis, his wearing apparell and money in
his purse.   03.00.00

Item. six Bushells of wheat in the house at 6d. per bushell.	01.06.00
Item. one bushells of mault in the house.	00.03.00
Item. three bushells of pease and fitches.	00.06.09
Item. ten bushells of tailing oates.	00.15.00
Item. In his Lodging Chamber one bed and bedstedde and all thereunto belonging.	02.10.00
Item. In his chamber one copher one side cupbbord and one old fourme.	00.06.08
Item. In the hall chamber one flocke bedd and bedstead and all thereto belonging, one chest and four small cophers with some other lumber.	02.03.04
Item. In the chamber over his chamber one hull bedd and bedstedde and all thereto belonging.	00.13.04
Item. Two payers of sheetes, 2 tablecloths, one dozen of napkins and 2 pillow coates.	01.00.00
Item. Flax and linen yarn in the house.	00.07.00
Item. 4 tubbs; 1 oiuer with other lumber.	00.08.00
Item. In the Butterye 1 barrell, 4 firkins, 1 bruing tub, 1 lantern.	00.10.00
Item. In the kitchen 1 table, 8 milk truggs, 1 silting . . . cheese press; and 1 sadle with other lumber.	01.00.00
Item. In the hall, 1 cupboard, 1 table, 1 forme and 1 bench.	00.10.00
Item. 3 Chaires, 1 cradle and cushion with some other lumber.	00.10.00
Item. The pewter vessell.	00.16.00
Item. All the brasse vessells and 1 pewter chamber pot.	00.15.00
Item. 3 iron potts, 1 iron kettle, 3 iron skillets, 2 firing pans, 2 small spitts, 2 paires of pott hangers, 1 pair gridgirons, 1 cleaver, 1 paire of tongs.	00.12.00
Item. 3 buckets, 3 wooden platters, half a dozen dishes and some other lumber.	00.04.00
Item. All his working tooles belonging to his Trade.	01.14.00
Item. 3 sackes and 2 leatherne baggs.	00.05.00
Item. 4 Keene.	13.00.00
Item. 1 mare and 2 colts.	05.00.00
Item. 4 young hoggs at 12s.6d. a peere.	02.10.00
Item. 4 stalls of bees.	01.00.00
Item. The Geese, the duckes and hennes.	00.07.00
Item. 1 Grindstone.	00.01.00
Item. 2 acres of wheate.	04.00.00

	£. s. d.
Item. 5 acres of oates, peas and fitches.	03.16.00
Item. 4 hoggs of bacon.	05.00.00
Item. 1 harrow and trazes belonging thereto.	00.05.00
Summa	54.03.05

An item which appears with rather surprising regularity in even modest inventories — as with its rather shaky arithmetic — is a dozen or so of napkins reflecting perhaps the need to protect clothing while feeding. Table forks were introduced from Italy in 1601 but were not yet among the equipment of the working people.

The relatively prosperous Thomas Luxford's inventory is given below in full;[7] it presents a picture of a very decent house with a parlour and best chamber (the hall house has given place to the two-storied dwelling), a kitchen, and over these are upper chambers, including one over the entry, a passage wide enough for a cart to pass between the house and outhouses. The absence of any mention of carts, here and in other inventories, seems strange.

An inventory of the Goods and Chattels of Thos. Luxford[8] of Choluck, Colier. Dec'd. Apprised by those whose names are hereunder written this 3rd Day June 1712.

		£. s. d.
Item.	Ready money and waring apparrell.	05.00.00
,,	Bills and bonds and book debts.	50.00.00
,,	In the Kitchen a clock, table, 9 chairs, and dresser. 1 warming pan, looking glass, 1 pr. pot hooks, 1 fierpan, 1 pr. tongs, 1 pr. bellows, 1 pr. andirons, spit and dripon pan. 4 Candlesticks, 1 pr. snuffers, 1 peper box, 1 flower box, 1 salt box, 2 skilletts, 1 doz & half plates, 5 pewter dishes, 1 curtain.	04.01.00
,,	in ye Parlor 1 Table, 8 chairs, 2 Andirons.	01.01.06
,,	in ye Milkhouse; 4 beear cask, 2 brine tubbs, 6 milk vessels, 1 dresser, 1 pr. butter scales, a platter, 1 frying pan, 2 keelers, 2 stalders, 1 churn.	01.08.06
,,	in the brewhouse. 1 copper, 4 Tubbs, 2 keelers. 1 pr. scales, 3 pails, 1 hog tub and Washingblock, 2 iron pots, 1 wortsive . . . (illegible) & tungus.	
,,	In ye Drinkhouse 1 stalder, 3 barrols and som old lumber.	00.12.00
,,	in ye best chamber, 1 bed as it stands, a Chest of drawers, 1 Table, 1 looking glass, 7 Chayors, fiorpan and Tongues,	

Item.	4 window curtains, pair creepers.	07.05.00
,,	In ye chamber over ye milkhouse. 1 bed	
	as it stands. 2 Chayors, 1 Trunk.	03.00.00
,,	In ye chamber over ye Kitchen, 1 bed	
	as it stands, 1 chest, 1 chayor, 1	
	hanging press, 5 pr. sheetes, 4 pr.	
	pillowboards, 4 table cloths, 1 doz.	
	Napkins, 6 Towels, 4 Silver Spoons.	08.04.06
,,	In ye Chamber over ye Entrey. 1	
	Truckol bed 15 pounds of Linon yarne	
	and some olde lumber.	00.15.00
,,	Without doors, 2 Cowes & a . . .	
	(illegible).	06.00.00
,,	one Mare, 8 sheep 2 Hoggs.	09.15.00
,,	6 Acres Barly.	11.00.00
,,	3 Acres Sanfoine.	02.05.00
,,	900 laths coopers Ash Timber fior	
	wood, harrow, 2 logstocks, 1 Cribb, 6	
	Gates.	04.00.00
,,	Wood in Longbeach.	40.10.06
,,	Wood in Kits Wood, 46 Cord & a	
	quarter Brush and Ribbwood in ye	
	same.	28.02.06
,,	22 Cord and half of wood bought of	
	Dan Knowles.	11.05.00
,,	25 Cord of Cherrytree wood at	
	hearnhill.	10.10.00
,,	Coal Sacks and Coaling materials.	06.05.00
,,	Things unseen and forgotten.	00.10.06
		130.03.06
	at ye otherside	83.19.00
	Sum Totall	214.02.06
	Giles Hilton	
etc.	Sm. Rucke,	

Note: Creepers are andirons — firedogs.
A wortsive is a brewing sieve.
Keelers are shallow tubs used for milk to cool.

Edward Luxford (1681) of Charing, near Choluck,[9] was not directly related to Thomas Luxford. Living one generation earlier in a small house with a hall, which he did not own, he had a chamber over the hall, a wash house, a chamber over the wash house, a milk house and a drinkhouse. He also had a few farm animals and his estate was valued at £42.10.06. His will is marked with his mark, not signed.

The least prosperous of the colliers in this 17th and 18th century group drawn for reference was Denham Baker[10] of Hatfield in East Sussex who died in 1717. He owned his house and his total possessions were priced at £33.13.0. These included two small tables, three old chairs, a form, a warming pan, clothing-and-money-in-his-purse worth £1.0.0., two small chests, a small trunk and two cupboards, with some domestic objects. He had two beds, an ordinary bed and steadle and all belonging to it, worth 15/-., and another bed and steadle and all belonging to it, worth 35/-. He had only one small hogg, worth 15/-., and the house, with a small parcel of land, was valued at £26.

Wearing apparel and money in the purse vary in value between five pounds and one pound, and it is interesting to notice that both John Purkiss and Edward Luxford make bequests to their daughters of one shilling, or, as the latter expresses it, twelve pence.

These wills and inventories do not suggest great wealth although Thomas Luxford was probably "comfortably off".

John Purkiss, although owning a house, seems not to have had money to hand in any great quantity and was uncertain whether a part of his land might have to be sold to pay off his debts.

Inventories held in Staffordshire[11] include those of the goods of four colliers during the 18th century. Of these, the highest total is £50.14.0., and the lowest £6.13.0., the dates being 1715 and 1717 respectively. The other two total between seventeen and twenty pounds and are dated 1747 and 1752.

All of these inventories include domestic animals, among which figure those belonging to Edward Turner of Cannock Wood:

Cattle, 3 cows and one calf, the distemper
    being within a mile of the place . . . . £8.0.0.
A small two year old filly, with
    15 poor old sheep . . . . £5.2.0.

Some comparisons from "Village Records"[12] for 1668 are interesting.

A Kidderminster clothier's inventory totalled £22.4.0., that of a Kidderminster seamstress, £99.1.10. — but of that over £80 were materials of her trade; an Evesham joiner's inventory totalled £101.6.6. but of that £63 was for timber; and a poor Cordwainer's estate was valued at £1.14.0. (which included two bedsteads).

It would seem that from the sixteenth to the late eighteenth centuries, colliers were men of fixed abode, some literate enough to sign their names, others not so, and that they frequently rented smallholdings on which to raise a few acres of crops and kept a few animals if they did not own their own homesteads. Some rose in the world. John Sadler of Brightling,[13] described as a collier when named as a party to title deeds at an earlier date, in his will of 1610, is described as a yeoman and was able to bequeath "Unto Susanna my wife for the term of her natural life the whole messuage and tenaments barn and other edifices and appurtenances with the land thereto belonging containing in all by estimation some fourteen acres more or less lying and being in the Parish of name of Broadfield in Sussex and commonly called by the name of 'Bakers and Tanners'."

Among the Bewdley borough records, Mr. C. J. Bond found apprenticeship indentures "to teach the business of woodcollier" dated 1762 and 1763; in 1773 a woodcollier of Ribbesford near Bewdley, named Humphrey Crow, figures in a tripartite indenture in the Bewdley tanyard deeds, and through the Kelly's Directory for Bewdley, he traced the advance of Mr. Joseph Oakes who appeared first as a charcoal burner in 1884 to becoming, between 1896 and 1916, a "timber merchant, farmer and charcoal dealer", holding during this period a year of office as Mayor of Bewdley.

During the sixteenth century, London was growing very quickly and the supply of charcoal to households in the city and its suburbs kept busy the charcoal burners of Surrey, Kent and Essex, within reach of the capital. Croydon[14] in particular had a reputation as the centre both of charcoal burning and of smithing. A notice of the old town written in the reign of Queen Elizabeth I says that "The streets were deep hollow ways and very dirty, the houses generally with wooden steps into them, and darkened by large trees growing before them — and the inhabitants in general were smiths and colliers". The condition remained for some time, as in 1662, Patrick Hannay published a poem with more information on the same subject:

In midst of these stands Croydon cloath'd in black
    In a low bottome sinke of all these hills
And those who there inhabit suting well
With such a place do either nigros seem
    Or harbingers for Pluto prince of hell.
                . . . .
The unpav'd lanes with muddie mire it fills
    If one shower fall, or if that blessing stay,
You may well smell, but never see your way.

This view — or rather scent — of Croydon was not unperceived by an Archbishop of Canterbury (Bishop Grindall) whose archepiscopal palace nearby was permeated by smoke to the discomfort of His Grace and His Grace's entourage. The offending collier was called Francis Grimes, and in 1568 the Archbishop brought a lawsuit against him, requiring that the nuisance should cease. A jury of twelve men, however, found for the defendant on the grounds that he had to carry on his trade. This Francis Grimes[15] lived at a farmhouse called Colliers Water, which later was occupied by the John Gilpin (a gentleman of credit and renown) whose ride to Edmonton became the subject of well-known comic verses by William Cowper (1731-80). Grimes figured subsequently in a play "The Saucy Collier of Croydon and the Devil" —

the devil being supposed to represent the haughty Primate Ecclesiasticus.

In his article, already cited, Mr. Morewood Dowsett comments that Grimes was one of twenty colliers then active in Croydon, obtaining their charcoal from the woods extending from Norwood and Dulwich via Sydenham and Penge to Croydon.

The imagination of London's poets and playwrights was somehow excited by blackness of face, particularly of the colliers, whom they associated frequently with the Devil, who again is sometimes called "the collier in Hell". Greene, in his "Quip for an Upstart Courtier" (1592) has the line "Marry, quoth he that look't like Lucifer, though I am black I am not the divell but indeed a Collyer of Croydon". Shakespeare in "Twelfth Night", in the baiting of Malvolio has Sir Toby advise him not to play cherrypit with Satan; "hang him, foul collier!", and in another comedy of 1568, Ulpean Fulwel's "Like wil to like Quod thee Devil to the Colier" three of the characters, Tom Collier, Nichol Newfangle and the Devil, dance together to the tune of "Tom Collier of Croidon hath solde his cole".

The rising price of charcoal probably played its part in strengthening the Satanic association. Richard Crowley in the middle of the sixteenth century wrote a satirical epigram on the subject of the Collier of Croydon:

It is said that in Croydon there did sometyme dwell
A Collyer that did al other Colyers excel,
For his riches thys collyer might have been a Knight,
But in the order of Knighthood he had no delight;
Would God al our Knights did mind coling no more
Than thys collyer did Knighting, as is sayd before:
For when none but pore collyers did with coles mell;
At a reasonable price they did their coles sell;
But since our Knight collyers have had the first sale,
We have pay'd much money, and had few sacks to tale;
A lode, that late years for a royal was sold,
Wyl cost now XVI shillings of sylver or gold.
God graunt these men grace their polling to refrayne.
Or else bryng them back to theyre old state agayne;
And especially the Colliar that at Croydon doth dwell.
For men think he is cosin to the collyar in hell.

In "Damon and Pythias" by Richard Edwards, first acted in 1566, one of the characters is Grimme the Collier of Croydon; and in 1662 a satirist, "J.T.", wrote a comedy "Grim the Collier of Croydon, or the Devil and his Dame".

On the other hand the line occurs in the Egloges of Alexander Barkley:

"And as in Croiden I heard the Collier preache"

reminding us that this was the era of the Reformation.

It is difficult to understand the structure of this section of society. It seems probable that the rich colliers were successful employers who might become, if not knights, yeomen*, that there was a middle stratum of charcoal producers perhaps working alongside their burners, and there were the burners themselves about whom we know very little except that if their masters' faces were black, theirs were certainly blacker. The claim is sometimes made that a collier is always a master and a burner the man who did the work, but there seems no absolute rule about this. A report from an Elizabethan pamphlet illustrates how confusing the coaling business could be. In "A Notable Discovery of Coosnage, 1591 (Plainely laying open those pernitious sleights that hath brought many ignorant men to confusion)", Robert Greene discourses on a malpractice in the retail sale of charcoal. In the city of London, strict controls were exercised to assure that the measuring of coals was exact. To avoid Her Majesty's officers, certain dealers, here called "legers", had houses in the suburbs — "at Shoreditch, Whitechappel, Southwark and such places" with a yard or back gate "convenient for their cosening purpose . . . the Leger, the crafty collier I meane, riseth very early in the morning, and either goeth towards Croydon, Whetstone, Greenwitch, or Romford, and there meeteth the country colliers, who bring coles to serve the market: there, in a forestalling manner, this leger bargayneth with the Countrie Collier for his coales, and paieth for them nineteen shillings or twentie at the most, but commonly fifteene and sixteene, and there is in the load 36 sackes: so that they pay for every couple about fourteen pence. Now, having bought his coales, everie sack containing full foure bushels, he carrieth the Countrie Collier home to his legering place, and there at the back gate causeth him to unload . . . then the Leger who hath three or four hired men under him bringeth forth his own sacks which be long and narrow holding at the most not three bushels, so they gaine in the change of everie sack a bushel for their pains" . . . Furthermore, the dross is put at the bottom of the sacks and the top is best filled to make a fair show. "Then a tall sturdie knave, that is all ragged and durtie on his legs as thogh he came out of the Countrie (for they durtie theyr hose and shoos on purpose to make themselves seem countrie colliers:). Thus with two sacks a peece they either go out of the back gate or steal out at the street side, and go up and downe the suburbs, and sel their coales in summer for fourteene and sixteene pence a couple, and in winter for eighteene or twentie. The poore cookes and other citizens that buy them, thinke they be countrie colliers, that have left some coles of their load and would gladly have monie, and have but two bushels and a half for foure bushels and yet are extremely rakt in the price."

We are further told that Her Majesty's officers in London look carefully to the country coals and "if they finde not four bushels in everie sack do sell to the poor as forfeit, and distribut the mony to them that have need, burning the sacke and honoring or rather dishonoring the pillerie with the Colliers durty faces". One learns that the limit the Statute sets as a penalty is whipping at a cart's tail. Greene continues with an account of the anger of a woman so defrauded:

> "For fewell or firing being a thing necessary in a common wealth, and charcole used more than any other, the poore not able to buy by the load, are fain to get in their fire by the sacke, and so are greatly coosned by the retaile" . . .
> "I heard with my eares a pore woman of Shoreditch who had bought coles of a leger, with weeping teares complain and raile against him in the streete, in her rough eloquence calling him a coosning knave, and saying, 'tis no marvell, villain,' (quoth she) 'if men compare you colliers to the devill, seeing your consciences are worser than the devilles, for hee takes none but those souls whom God hates: and you undo the poore whome God loves'.
> "What is the matter good wife (quoth I) that you use such invective words against the collier: 'a collier, sir (saith she) he is a theefe and a robber of the common people. Ile tel you sir, I bought of a Countrie collier two sackes for thirteen-pence and I bought of this knave three sackes, which cost me 22 pence: and sir, when I measured both of their sackes, I had more in the two sackes by three pecks, than I had in the three, I would' (quoth she) 'the Justices would looke into this abuse, and that my neighbours would joyne with me in a suppli-cation, and by God I would kneele before the Queene, and intreat that such coosening Colliers might not only bee punished with the bare pillerie, (for they have such blacke faces that no man knowes them again, and so they are careles), but that they might leave their eares behinde them for a forfeit: and if that would not mend them, that *Bul* with a faire halter might root them out of the world . . .' The collier hearing this, went smiling away because he knew his life was not lokt into and the woman wept for anger that she had not some one by that might with justice revenge her quarrell."

Richard Crowley would have had to wait some time for his wish that God might "Bring them back to theyr old state agayne" to appear to be granted but the last echo of the diabolic tradition seems to be found in lines by Christopher Smart (1722-70) describ-ing hop drying in Kent over a charcoal fire made from discarded hop poles, which "The sable priests of Vulcan shall prepare". Vulcan, by this time, was moving on, and very soon his sable priests would work with picks and wagons underground.

By the early twentieth century, when the charcoal burning industry had dwindled to very little, it was easy, seeing the unusual sight of a cabin and a kiln in the wood, to suppose it had not changed since the days of the legendary Purkis. For the most part it was carried on as a seasonal occupation. W. R. Butterfield[16] reported that "Older men remember a time when they were continuously employed from April to November each year. At present all charcoal that is required is made during the few weeks before hop-picking and the price has dropped from 9d. per bushel to 4d. The collier and his mate move from farm to farm as required and cover a wide area each season". He also noted that "At one time farmers supplied home brewed ale; and "swanky", a small beer at village provision shops, was 2d. per quart".

In Cumbria, burning was carried out at the turn of the century during the late summer and autumn. In the Wyre Forest, burning took place all through the year, and in all these cases the burners had a cottage within visiting distance where the families lived and to which the men went home when they could. Food was brought out to them; they were essentially "local people". On the other hand, the Francis family moved always — at about six months' intervals — burning charcoal where the timber was ready for them on a "piece work" basis. The policy developed at the end of the eighteenth century for some merchants and manufacturers to send their own burners to work in the woods and this sometimes led to friction with local burners.[17] Mrs. Langridge does not remember that her family ever encountered any hostility; by the beginning of this century there were probaly so few local burners that their ways did not cross. The fuel merchants arranged the family's itinerary, and paid for the wood, which was cut ready for making into kilns; they also collected the charcoal (returning it, if through bad weather, it had become damp) and arranged the family's transport when the next removal became due. This nomadic way of life may reflect the need for a survival adaptation when the industry in the south decayed so drastically.

Be that as it may, for the Francis family, home was a series of turf covered huts built when and where they were needed. The children were sent to school at the nearest village, perhaps four miles away, and brought back with them whatever was needed from the shop — which, as Mrs. Langridge points out, was not much.

The sack of flour for the weekly batch of loaves — the staple diet — the father brought home. This was supplemented with skimmed milk, which could be bought before 1914 at 1d. per gallon at the nearby farms, and small or cracked eggs unsuitable for the market. The farmers also allowed cheap vegetables, sometimes even free for the taking, and it was possible to buy cheap cuts from the butcher, such as breast of mutton, at a few pence a pound, or, if one went late on a Saturday — before the days of refrigeration in the village shops — it might be almost given away. It may be that the Francis family received very friendly treatment. "Dad" was a member of the Salvation Army and they enjoyed attending the services and joining in the singing. Photographs of other charcoal burners also suggest an ordered way of life. J. G. Jenkins[18] illustrates his charcoal burning section with an idyllic picture, but the Wyre Forest records[19] include rougher incidents, even including a rumour that one burner accidentally killed his nagging wife and cremated her in a kiln. Mr. Bond[20] quotes in his notes a record of nocturnal assault, in 1221, by two charcoal burners on a Beadle and his wife, which was brutal and violent by either medieval or modern standards; but such outrage does not seem linked with any particular occupation. From Mr. Nevey, Mr. Bond heard of a charcoal burner reputed to have lived entirely on tea. He worked by himself and was generally known as Jimmy Shady, but was also called Jimmy Slash. Mr. Norris, writing of Cumbrian memories, draws attention to the mysterious appellation of a charcoal burner known as Pharoah, the Egyptian, remembered as having been prevailed upon to present his fifteen children, already assembled, for baptism. Whether or not this Pharoah was a gypsy, as his name might suggest, is unknown. An Anthonie Romanie is named in the Watermillock records for 1581, and in 1614 "Pharoah" and in 1767 "Egypt" are found used in the position of baptismal names in Hawkshead.

In the more southern counties tales are told of how to charm a game bird out of a tree and how to cook it inside a thick crust of clay; head, feathers, claws, entrails and all, in the fire. When it was cooked, the feathers came off with the clay and the entrails were easily separable from the meat.[21] Mr. Nevey, who supplied the recipe — though not the instructions for catching the bird — also gave two more cooking hints. The smell of smoke could be removed from tea by dropping a little charcoal into it, and meat cooked together with pieces of charcoal will lose any tainted flavour it might have. It is fair to suppose snared rabbits found their way to the pot of many charcoal burners. Snails roasted in hot ash are among other items listed of woodland diet[22] but no one now claims to have eaten them. Walter Rose, however, the author of "Good Neighbours", tells there that he ate snails raw as they were locally reputed to be a cure and preventative for the dreaded "consumption" — tuberculosis. He found them delicious!

Very different was the food of the burners in the Lake District. Round the Furness area, charcoal burning was a seasonal occupation and with the continuing use of charcoal by the furnaces — Backbarrow furnace used it until 1926 — prices were good. Mr. Allonby, asked about his experience, wrote "The standard of living, as I knew it, so far as food was concerned, was very high. Nothing but the best was taken to the wood in charcoaling time. I can only speak for my own family and for the Ellwood family. They all had small-holdings on which they kept pigs, hens and cows. I remember, as a small boy, my father having two pigs —

which I sometimes had to feed. They were kept especially for
coaling time. He always hired four men and fed them during the
coaling season. This, with him, would start in September and go on
right up to Christmas and sometimes into the New Year''. Here
conditions are reminiscent of those suggested by some of the wills
and inventories already examined. Even so, it was not a life without
rigours; Cumbrian home-based burners would sometimes travel up
to twenty miles to the forest encampments.

Signature of John Purkiss
on his will, 1672.

1. Hut construction at the Weald & Downland Open Air Museum at Singleton, Sussex. Setting up the poles.

2. Hut construction, covering with sacks and turf; twigs to "key" the turves are stuck into the upper course of turf.

3.   Mr. and Mrs. Langridge before the completed hut.

4.   A corner of the hut interior, showing a bed.

5. Living huts. The one in the foreground has a sacking curtain which can be let down over the door. The frontispiece and Plates 31 and 38 are of the same series as this and it is thought the encampment may have been near Slindon.

6. A hut covered with sacks held in place by poles and a few large-headed nails. This photograph was taken in the Wyre Forest, in the 1930s.

HUT BUILDING

An article in "Gwerin", December 1958, entitled "Charcoal Burners' Huts and Hut Circles"[1] made the point that the debris of charcoal huts would closely resemble that of hut circles of very early date and that these burners' huts show such uniformity as would not be expected unless they had a common origin. This may be arguable — the concial hut is an extremely practical way of building with unsophisticated materials and the wigwam of American origin bears this out without being possibly related to charcoal burners' cabins. On the other hand, it is true that in Europe, of woodland workers, only charcoal burners use this one particular type of shelter, though on occasion, as in Cumbria, they are willing to utilise the huts of other craftsmen. In the Roman campagna, other workers also used the same huts as the charcoal burners. It may safely be said that the conical cabin, which can be found in Lapland and in Italy, represents a primitive form of building with a very long history.

The huts of an encampment show variations from place to place and within the limited scope here attempted are best considered separately.

The Francis family huts were about ten feet in diameter and made of sixteen poles of twelve to fourteen feet in length, some of which forked at the top, all meeting at the apex of the cone and tied together. (Plate 1). Six horizontal pieces formed a girdle around this construction, leaving a place open for the door, and they were tied to the long poles — which were about six or seven inches thick at the base — with cord. Over this cone, sacks were put to make a lining for the hut and, then, starting at ground level, of course, brushwood twigs — leafy if possible — were stuck all around at an angle to "key" the turf covering (Plate 2), which was stacked like bricks, grass side uppermost in horizontal courses. When the brushwood twigs were nearly covered a second stage could be added, and then more turf until the top was reached. (Plate 3). The porch, giving headroom and shelter from rain, was brought forward when the poles were first set in position; the illustration shows how this was arranged. Inside the hut, two beds, one to either side of the porch with a passageway between were made of stakes placed longways and held by shorter staves driven into the ground at the ends; these were "sprung" with brushwood and made more comfortable with a mattress of strawfilled sacks. (Plate 4, Plate 5). Sacks provided a door or curtain which could be turned back over the porch roof when not needed. A brazier of burning charcoal could be put in the doorway of the hut but was never left there overnight, however cold the weather, because of the danger from fumes — the hut had no opening except for the doorway. It must have been a hard life, but Mrs. Francis, who was a farmer's daughter, is said never to have complained. For the children, "life was like that"; one did not question it. The drying of clothes was the biggest domestic problem — and, in bad weather with a large family (there were ten children), it must have been nearly insoluble, even although the elder children would leave home to start work while still young.

A wet period could also mean a serious lack of money, though with very good weather, a kiln "in advance" might be managed to even things out. To build a kiln and burn a kiln in a week — and dismantling a kiln would be included in this — was a usual programme and, before the First World War, Mr. Francis could expect to earn between 20/- and 30/- for this. As a family wage, it seems hopelessly small but at that time a junior artisan — say, a silversmith in his twenties — would be earning about thirty shillings also.

One year, Mr. Francis built a day hut in which to accommodate his family during a particularly wet autumn. It was as if two of the conical huts had been merged with a long connecting section. The hut is shown in some of the Singleton Museum photographs. It was very useful as it offered facilities for a kitchen and dining room, far superior to what the small huts could afford. The mother could make bread or piecrust on the long table, ready to be baked at the external oven (a metal drum set horizontally in a bank and lagged with turf in which a half faggot was burned to give sufficient stored heat, as in many a farmhouse oven). When the oven was thought to be hot enough, the burning embers were raked out and the bread went in at the back, the pies at the front. The door was closed with a wet sack against which an iron sheet was propped. Outside was a fire over which a kettle and a stewpot could be hung.

Inside the day hut, in addition to its plank table, a long box made a seat and doubled as a wardrobe. The two rounded ends gave extra bed space. This particular hut was never repeated perhaps because of the coming of the war when Mr. Francis joined the army and the family went to live in a house. The one at the Museum also, although it aroused much interest and was authentic in that it had played a part in the way of life of actual charcoal burners, has been taken down as not sufficiently traditional to warrant inclusion.

While the family lived in the woods, basket-making and besom-making sometimes earned a few extra pence.

When Mrs. Langridge, then still a little girl, first lived in a house, she says they all found it "scarey"; while indoors there was a feeling that "something might happen" but the comfort of a cottage was soon appreciated. To Mrs. Francis it would seem a return to normal conditions. By the time the father returned Mrs. Langridge was old enough to go into service and leave home.

Mr. Langridge learned charcoal burning as a part-time trade from his father-in-law and, while the older man was a burner, he was willing to cut and burn, or to burn only, as the work required.

The period between the wars was one of hard times for country-folk. Two pounds a week was a good wage. A cowman received ten shillings a week, with a cottage, a little garden, "what vegetables you like" from the farm and two pints of milk a day. Mr. Langridge was a young man on a farm, earning fourteen shillings and his keep each week when his father died — leaving him with seven people to support. As a boy, he earned 2/6d. for seven days a week and at nineteen, this was stepped up to 6d. per day.

W. R. Butterfield[2] writing about charcoal burning in the south of England mentions huts of a less substantial kind, "usually only sailcloth on a clumsy framework", and the standard "Wyre Forest" huts, as reported by Mr. Bond, were of wigwam form consisting of a tripod of timbers lashed at the top, resting on the ground surface, with further timbers leaning up against these to complete the circumference of the hut and covered with several layers of sacks, not tied in any way, held in position by the weight of further staves placed on top. (Plate 6).

It is reported that they were fairly weather proof and warm to sleep in. Mr. Wilde[3] relates that similar cabins were covered with canvas and turf and that the floor was covered with a thick layer of fine birch twigs, except for a circular space in the centre where a charcoal fire was lit before occupancy and never allowed to go out while the cabin was in use. A small hole at the apex of the cabin served as a vent — sufficiently so as to prevent carbon monoxide poisoning. The calculated risk of fire danger would seem to outweigh that of the fumes! It cannot be assumed that the sacks-only covering was merely a stage towards turf covering — such huts are illustrated in a photograph from the Stone Collection in the Birmingham Reference Library, dated 1896, and another photograph taken in the Ribbersford Woods, south of Wyre, c. 1920 exists, as well as one in the Hartlebury Castle collection of the same date and place as Plate 33, 1956.

Mr. Hazeldine Warren writing in 1910[4] reported on a hut built at Cuckoo Pits, near Chingford, Essex. This was conical, about twelve feet in diameter. (Plate 7). It had a framework of twelve poles, saplings of four inches diameter at the bottom ends, and the outer slope from top to ground level was about twelve feet. The poles, some of which were forked at the top, were placed in a circle leaning inwards and met at about eighteen inches from their ends. At the meeting points some poles were rested within the forks of others and they were lashed together (as in the case of the "Langridge" hut). The main poles were further fastened by three or four cross bearers between each two poles — the poles being spaced rather irregularly with gaps of twenty-six to forty inches between them. Between the cross bearers, the space was filled with a number of smaller pieces, one and a half to two inches in diameter, resting on the cross bearers. The whole was then covered by fifteen to sixteen courses of sods, or turf with the grass sides

7. This photograph is of great interest in that it shows turves in the "tiling" style, not supported by exterior poles or weights. It was taken in the Epping Forest area in 1910.

8. This hut, which is of a kind that bark-peelers in Cumbria used to construct, was also taken over for use when an unoccupied one was situated at a convenient place by charcoal burners of the district. It temporarily constituted a family dwelling and had some simple furniture within.

turned inwards, overlapping each other like tiles on a roof. This hut
had a porch in the manner of the Langridge hut. How these turves
were held in place is not mentioned. Within were two beds, with a
gangway three feet wide between them. The beds were made of
three heavy logs placed on the ground, with cross bearers of smaller
boughs and cushioned with straw. A brazier of charcoal for heating
could be put in the doorway.

Mr. James Walton notes that the charcoal burner's huts of
south Yorkshire were similar to those of this Epping Forest hut but
the roofs were steeper — twelve or thirteen feet high, and quotes
Thomas Winder, writing in 1896, who stated that they were built of
a number of poles laid together to form a cone, placed about nine
inches apart and interlaced with brushwood. The doorway was
formed by laying a lintel from fork to fork and the whole covered
with sods laid grass sides inwards. There is no mention of a porch.
One cannot be dogmatic about these differences — photographs
exist showing a very steep hut, turf covered and without a porch,
from Sheffield Park, in Sussex, and another, which would seem of
more usual height, also without a porch, from Rockley, Stain-
borough, Yorkshire, reproduced in "The Welsh House", by I. C.
Peate.

In the High Furness district, an account of huts is complicated
by the fact that more substantial huts used by woodland workers
might also be used by charcoal burners if they were conveniently
situated and available.

The photograph shown in Plate 8 appeared in the North
Lonsdale Magazine and Furness Miscellany (1898) over the caption
"Charcoal Burners' Hut"; it is not what is understood in the
Furness Fells as a charcoal cabin but is known as a "Bark Peelers'
Hut" and the people in the photograph may well be bark peelers
(this being a summer occupation in the area) living there in relative
comfort — furniture is visible within the hurdle door and the lady
holds a silver teapot. These huts are made of double wattle walls,
infilled with bracken, and may be quite large — up to ten feet by
sixteen feet. Above the three foot vertical walls, turf covered roofs
are ingeniously supported by four poles, having their feet wedged
between two horizontal rails along the top of the outer wall
fencing and further supported by the corner uprights of the inner
fence, both fences having pointed lower ends well planted in the
ground. (Fig. 2a, A, B & C). The supporting poles may meet and be
tied at the top, as in the diagram, or they may support a roof tree.[5]

This type of cabin has a fireplace built very thickly of stone,
made airtight with packed earth. The back wall may be entirely of
stone or just the fireplace and chimney behind it. Stone reinforces
the doorway in the hut illustrated. Usually the huts are on sloping
ground, with the chimney built out behind on the highest part,
perhaps to a height of as much as eight feet above the floor level.
The hut shown in Plate 9, put up by Mr. Allonby for the demon-

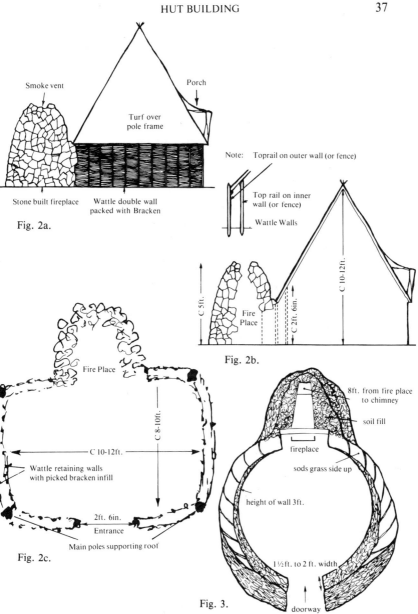

Fig. 2a.

Fig. 2b.

Fig. 2c.

Fig. 3.

2a, b, c. Cumbrian hut construction, side elevation, section and ground plan by
Mr. J. Allonby.

3.   Ground plan of a "living cabin", Cumbria, by Mr. J. Allonby.

stration burn at Ickenthwaite, had this kind of rectangular ground plan. The rather low chimney can be seen in the rear.

A second type of hut is known as a Living Cabin and these, Mr. Allonby says, were put up by wood cutters only, though they were used by colliers also if they were not too far from the kilns. Often the cutters worked for a master collier and shared the cabin with him. Most men lived in these cabins because their true homes were fifteen to twenty miles away, too far to walk to work each day. Mr. Allonby is seen in Plate 10 emerging from a cabin of this kind, which he built at Statterthwaite. It is circular in plan, has a fireplace (the chimney is just discernible in the photograph) and is stone walled entirely, the walls being between one and a half and two feet in thickness. On the top of these thick sods are placed, grass side up to prevent the roof supports from slipping. Four principal supports are tied together at the top and other poles, of a lighter sort, added until almost butting, as also in the case of the Bark Peelers' huts. (Fig. 3).

Both kinds of hut were then roofed with a covering of thin turves, preferably of heather, with the growth side downwards, put on in the manner of tiles and held in place with more poles leaning upon them. The thatch shown on the Ickenthwaite hut is not characteristic but was put on for convenience in setting up the demonstration. Mr. Allonby says that it is difficult nowadays to get turf sufficiently waterproof and adds that turf which has been dressed with lime lets in the damp.

The third hut (Fig. 4A) found in the Furness accounts — for there seems none still extant — is the charcoal burners' cabin. It had no vertical walls, no fireplace and no porch (as had the other two huts). It was constructed by lashing together the tops of three poles set as a tripod. The intervening spaces were filled with lighter poles, the ends of which on the ground formed a circle with the three larger poles. Above the gap left for the doorway, a lintel was fixed and over it shorter poles. Over this cone of wood, flat turves were laid in the manner of tiles — as for the roofing of the two other Lakeland style huts and for the Cuckoo Pits hut in Essex. (Plate 7).

In such a hut, three beds might be fitted (Fig. 4B). Tradition has it that in the Furness area charcoal burners worked in groups of three but, though this is a convenient number, Mr. Allonby does not say it was the rule. In the middle of the hut, three stones were set to contain a charcoal fire and a sack covered the doorway. Fumes escaped through a small hole in the roof. This cabin, unlike the others, which might be occupied for weeks at a time and where families might be housed, was thought of as something very temporary — to be taken down and rebuilt as the charcoaling went on. As Mr. Allonby says, "A five minute walk could be too far on a stormy night and a burning pit could be lost". Nocturnal watch seems to have been punctiliously kept; Mr. Langridge says he only

9. Charcoal burners' hut at Ickenthwaite, Cumbria. This was set up for a demonstration charcoal burn; the thatched roof is unorthodox. A small fire-place
built of stone can be seen in the rear wall.

10. A "living hut" set upon a circular ground plan, at Statterthwaite, Cumbria.
The fireplace projection is on the extreme right hand side of the picture and the
porch — with a head emerging — juts out opposite.

lost one kiln, and that was when in a violent thunderstorm, thinking it was sufficiently covered and protected from the wind and himself not liking to be under the trees, he went away for a time and left it.

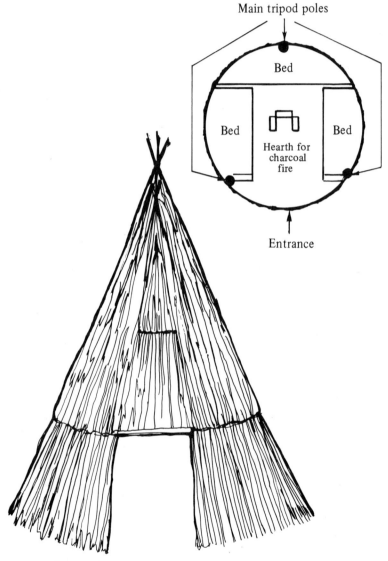

4. Frame and ground plan of a "charcoal burner's cabin", Cumbria, by Mr. J. Allonby.

THE CHARCOAL KILN

In October, 1662, John Evelyn, a gentleman of the Court (whose country estate was at Wooton in Surrey on the northern edge of the Weald) delivered a Discourse to the newly founded Royal Society concerning Forest Trees, which aroused much interest and was later printed with additions, and is known as "Sylva". Subsequently, it was revised and reprinted, and together with much information of great interest about forestry, it contains an account of charcoal making that in the twentieth century can hardly be bettered. (Edns. of 1679 and 1664).

He defines a cord as a "stack of wood (which is the boughs and offal of the trees to be converted to charcoal), four yards long, three and a half high (in some places but a yard) and as much over in other places . . . In other places the cord is four feet in height and four feet over" (i.e. across), "the content 128 cubic feet".

He continues:

"There is made of char-coal usually three sorts, viz. one for the Iron-works, a second for gunpowder, and a third for London and the Court, besides Small-coals of which we shall also speak in its due place.

We will begin with that sort which is us'd for the Ironworks, because the rest are made much after the same manner, and with very little difference.

The best Wood for this is good oak, cut into lengths of three foot, as they size it for the Stack: this is better than the Cord-wood, though of·a large measure, and much used in Sussex.

The Wood cut, and set in stacks ready for the Coaling, chuse out some level place in the Copp'ce, the most free from stubbs, etc. to make the Hearth on: in the midst of this area drive down a stake for your Centre, and with a pole, having a ring fastened to one of the extreams (or else with a Cord put over the Centre) describe a circumference from twenty or more feet semi-diameter, according to the quantity of your Wood designed for coaling, which being near may conveniently be Chared on that Hearth; and which at one time may be 12, 16, 20, 24, even to 30 stack: If 12 therefore be the quantity you will Coal, a circle whose diameter is 24 foot will suffice for the Hearth; if 20 Stack, a diameter of 32 foot; if 30, 40 foot, and so proportionably.

Having thus marked out the ground, with Mattocks, Haws, and fit instruments, bare it of the Turf, and of all other combustible stuff whatsoever, which you are to rake up towards the Peripherie, or out-side of the circumference, for an use to be afterwards made of it; plaining and levelling the ground with the Circle: This done the wood is to be brought from the nearest part where it is stacked in Wheel-barrows:

11. The commencement of a triangular flue at the Weald & Downland Open Air Museum. This is taken to a height of about three and a half feet, and the wood to be charred stacked against it.

12. Illustration to John Evelyn's book, "Sylva" (published in 1664), showing stages in kiln building. The flue started in the middle, with three staves laid on the ground is the same in principle as the contemporary one in Plate 11, which was a type used by charcoal burners until earth covered kilns were discontinued during this century. The short billets of wood in the kiln construction on the right do not resemble methods recently employed.

13. When the wood to be charred is in place, small wood of about one or two-inch diameter is set around and over it to help keep out draughts.

14. This illustration shows a notched tiller ladder set against the smoking kiln, and the upright poles of a style of flue still demonstrated in central Europe.

and first the smallest of it plac'd at the utmost limit, or very margin of the Hearth, where it is to be placed longways as it lay in the stack; the biggest of the Wood pitch, or set up on end round about against the small-wood, and all this within the Circle, till you come within five or six foot of the Centre: at which distance you shall begin to set the Wood in a Triangular form (Plate 11) till it come to be three foot high. Against this again, place your greater Wood almost perpendicular, reducing it from the Triangular to a Circular form, till having gained a yard or more you may pile the Wood longways as it lay in the Stack, being careful that the ends of the Wood do not touch the Pole which must now be erected in the centre, nine foot in height, that so there may remain a round hole, which is to be formed in working up the Stackwood, for a Tunnel, and the more commodious firing of the pit, as they call it, tho' not very properly. This provided for, go on to Pile, and set your Wood upright to the other as before; till having gained a yard or more you lay it long-ways again, as was shew'd; And thus continue the work, still enterchanging the position of the Wood, till the whole Area of the Hearth and Circle be filled and piled up at the least eight foot high, and so drawn in by degrees in Piling, that it resemble the form of a copped brown Household-loaf, filling all inequalities with the smaller Trunchions, till it lie very close, and be perfectly and evenly shaped. (Plates 12 & 13). This done, take straw, haume, or fern, and lay it on the outside of the bottom of the heap, or wood, to keep the next cover from falling amongst the sticks; upon this put on the Turf, and cast on the dust and Rubbish which was grubbed and raked up at the making of the Hearth, and reserved near the circle of it; and with this cover the whole heap of Wood to the very top of the Pit or Tunnel, to a reasonable and competent thickness, beaten close and even, that so the fire may not vent but in places where you intend it; and if in preparing the Hearth, at first, there did not rise sufficient Turf and Rubbish for this Work, supply it from some convenient place near to your heap: There be who cover this again with a sandy, or finer mould, which if it close well, need not be above an inch or two thick: This done, provide a Screene; by making light hurdles with slot rods, and straw of a competent thickness, to keep off the Wind, and broad, and high enough to defend an opposite side to the very top of your Pit, being eight or nine foot; and so as to be easily removed, as need shall requiring, for the luing of your pit. (Frontispiece & Plates 17, 26, 29, 34 & 36).

When now all is in this posture, and the wood well rang'd, and clos'd, as has been directed, set fire to your heap; But first you must provide you with a Ladder to ascend the

top of your Pit: This they usually make of a curved Tiller fit
to apply to the convex shape of the Heap, and cut it full of
notches for the more commodious setting of the colliers' feet
(Plate 14), whiles they govern the Fire above; when now they
pull up and take away the Stake which was erected at the
Centre, to guide the building of the Pile and cavity of the
Tunnel. This done, put in a quantity of Char-coals (about a
peck) and let them fall to the bottom of the Hearth; upon
them cast in Coals that are fully kindled; and when those that
were first put in are beginning to sink, throw in more fuel,
and so from time to time, till the Coals have universally taken
fire up to the top: Then cut an ample and reasonably thick
Turf, and clap it over the hole, or mouth of the Tunnel,
stopping it as close as may be with some of the former dust
and rubbish: Lastly, with the handles of your Rakers, or the
like, you must make Vent-holes, or Registers (as our
Chymists would name them) through the stuff which covers
your Heap to the very Wood, those in Rangers of two or three
foot distance, quite round within a foot (or thereabout) of the
top, tho' some begin them at the bottom: A day after begin
another row of holes a foot and a half beneath the former,
and so more, till they arrive to the ground, as occasion
requires. Note that as the Pit does coal and sink towards the
centre, it is continually to be fed with short and fitting Wood,
that no part remain unfired; and if it chars faster at one part
than at another, there close up the vent-holes, and open them
where need is: A Pit will in this manner be burning off and
charing, five or six days, and as it coals, the smoke from thick
and gross clouds, will grow more blue and livid, and the
whole mass sink accordingly; so as by these indications you
may the better know how to stop and govern your spiracles.
Two or three days it will only require for cooling, which (the
vents being stopped), they assist by taking now off the
outward covering with a Rabil or Rubler; but this, not for the
above space of one yard breadth at a time; and first remove
the coursest and grossest of it, throwing the finer over the
heap again, that so it may neither cool too hastily, nor
endanger the burning by reducing all to Ashes, should the
whole Pit be uncovered and expos'd to the Air at once;
therefore they open it thus round by degrees.

When now by all the former Symptoms you judge it fully
chared, you may begin to draw; that is, to take out the Coals,
first round the bottom, by which means the Coals, Rubbish
and Dust sinking and falling in together, may choke and
extinguish the fire.

Your Coals sufficiently cool'd, with a very long-tooth'd
Rake, and a Vann, you may lead them into the Coal Wains,

which are made close with boards, purposely to carry them to Market."

Although we are here concerned with earth covered kilns, the account which John Evelyn gives of the making of "small coals" is interesting. He says that these "Are made of the spray and brushwood which is stripped off from the branches of copp'se wood" and the wood being made up into small bundles or bavins. Then "setting one of the bavins on fire two men stand ready to throw on bavin upon bavin . . . so they have burnt all that lies near the place to the number of five or six hundred, but ere they begin to set fire they fill great tubs or vessels with water, and this they dash on with a great dish or scoop, so soon as ever they have thrown on all their bavins, continually plying the great heaps of glowing Coals, which gives a sudden stop to the fury of the fire, while with a great Rake they lay, and spread it abroad, and ply their casting of Water still on the Coals, which are now perpetually turn'd by two men with great Shovels, a third throwing on the Water: This they continue till no more Fire appears, tho' they cease not from being very hot: After this they shovel them up into great heaps and when they are thoroughly cold, put them up in sacks for London where they use them among divers artificers, both to kindle greater fires, and to temper and anneal their several works."

There is no knowledge of this method of burning among charcoal burners in England today. A recent verbal account given of a similar method used in some part of Africa was, unfortunately, not noted in any detail at the time. It is not general for that continent, at any rate, as it appears that in other parts the circular mound type of kiln is customary. In Rhodesia, for example; and elsewhere, a long mound, as in Kenya (Plates 15 & 16).

"A cord of wood" continues as a standard of measurement. 128 cubic feet, about a cartload, weighing about twenty-five hundredweight (but weights in relation to volume vary enormously with the degree of seasoning, this approximation being for relatively unseasoned wood). The length of the billet — which is known as "cordwood" (or "yardwood" in parts of the West Country) varies from between three and four feet. One cord would make a stack of about sixteen feet long, three and a half feet wide and three and a half high.

In reading "Sylva", a detail appears confusing: "Having gained a yard or more you may Pile the Wood longways as it lay in the Stack being careful that the ends of the wood do not touch the pole which must now be erected in the centre" and, in order to clarify, it may be best to recapitulate in brief the setting up of the kiln. First, a central flue is constructed — there are several forms this may take. The horizontally built triangular one, which John Evelyn describes, is shown in Plate 11, made by the continuous addition of three billets, tucking the meeting end of the third billet

15. A kiln smoking in Kenya.

16. The core of a kiln in Kenya, showing a long, low form which is fired through a hole in the narrow side when the earth covering is in place.

17. An engraving, probably of the 18th century and possibly of French origin, showing kilns burning. The conical styles are so different from anything now known that it may be supposed they are formalised — as are the neat spiracles of smoke in this and in Plate 12.

18. Another engraving from the same source as Plate 17, showing kiln building. The preparation of circular hearths is shown — letters A-C — and four ways of setting up a flue or central core — letters D-G and Fig. 1.

19. The central flue of an experimental kiln erected at the Blist Hill Museum, Coalbrookdale.

20. Kiln at Gutach Open Air Museum, Germany. A plugged draught-flue is situated just above ground level and around the kiln a walkway has been set up.

under that of the first at each stage to give greater security. This is built in the centre of a cleared and levelled circular area — the hearth — which may be sunken to the depth of a few inches, or cut into the slope of a hill.

As John Evelyn says, the size will be proportionate to the quantity of wood to be coaled, and the area must be checked to make certain that there are no burrows under the surface which would admit air. Around this, making a wall but with an opening to give entrance, cordwood is stacked with the thickest on the inside of the curve, set ready to hand, the thinner outside and some short pieces put aside. Outside this is a low bank of earth, sand or sods, for the final covering. When the "tunnel" (a vertical one) is the height of the cordwood's length, the stacked wood is set upright around it, leaning inwards a little along each of the three sides and in the angles of the overlapping ends. When the stack is six feet across — "having gained a yard or more" — the roofing tier is commenced. This is indeed done by laying on the wood longways, over the upright pieces, inclining upwards at the inner edge and letting the wood overlap a little sideways to accommodate the smaller circumference and raise the centre while keeping open a chimney hole, which now becomes not triangular but circular. In this type of flue a pole may be set to mark the centre when the open top of the chimney is no longer visible from below, and certainly, the billets must not touch this pole. The kiln can then be extended, first building out the walls, then the top and thickening the top so that at the inner rim it is about two feet thick and domed shape; curved staves may help to form the shoulder of the kiln, if not, this must be done by grading so that a smooth contour is achieved.

The kiln shown in Plate 12, is of many tiers but it seems probable it was not drawn "from nature"; one can assume, however, from this and from Plates 17 and 18 — again "naturalistically" impossible — that many tiered kilns were built.

In Plate 17, the initial structure of two flues and a more advanced stage of a third can be seen, all different from the one which has been described. In the left hand upper and right hand lower corner, long poles supported by diagonally placed stakes are set up, and this was the type of flue adopted in an experimental kiln built at the Blist Hill Museum, Coalbrookdale (Plate 19).

The constructions at "D" and "G" (Plate 17) are interesting, but cannot now, it would seem, be explained. No first-hand experience has been found of the use of a horizontally placed "floor" of ·wood making the burning hearth in this country, although Mr. Jack Allonby, whose family practised "coaling" for at least three generations in Cumbria, remembers being shown a raft-like base set for a kiln with the wood radiating outwards, one layer thick. In this illustration, the height and pitch of the conical kilns seem impossible, but one cannot be certain that they have no relation to kilns which in fact were constructed; other details, such as the type of wheelbarrow, the adze-like "stocker", the long-handled rake and shovel, are realistically observed tools which continued in use into this century.

This illustration and its companion (Plate 18) is probably French and of the eighteenth century. A kiln reconstructed at the Open Air Museum at Gutach, in the Black Forest region of Germany, is set upon a raft or wooden floor referred to in the English translation of the "Guidebook" as a "grate of round and split logs", surrounding the chimney vent and on which the wood for charcoaling is set. The grate as it is visible in the reconstruction is of carpentered planks giving a level surface which seems perhaps to be a compromise to stability rather than a reproduction of week to week practice in working conditions. This kiln (Plate 20) has draught channels at the base, one of which can be seen, plugged with a short length of round timber, in the illustration. It is a large kiln — nearly eight yards across — of three tiers and around it footboards supported by logs have been placed. These would help to hold the covering in position and provide a working platform. A photograph referred to below of a Swedish kiln shows what appear to be very long bladed raubers (Fig. 6 — there called "A cooler") placed almost continuously at two levels about the pile, but here the purpose must have been to support the cover as the single handles supporting the blades would not have provided balanced support for a footway. The Gutach kiln, covered by a wooden roof for protection, although left open in one section to show the construction, was too shaded for a satisfactory photograph of the interior to be possible.

Also from a continental Open Air Museum, that at Maria Saal, in Austria, come the photographs of a central flue which is the same as that used at Gutach. (Plates 21 & 22). This "Quandelschacht" (chimney vent) is of three round timbers held together by three iron rings. This kiln is built directly onto the ground; the top covering protected by polythene can be distinguished at the lower outside corners where it protrudes a little.

The uncovered kiln shown in Plate 14 appears to have a "Quandelschacht" core. Flues which survived into recent times in this country require separate description. One which would appear to be very common is the setting up of a central stake longer than the kiln will be high — so that it may be pulled out — around which firm uprights are set to make a kind of long box which will stay in place when the central pole is withdrawn. Plate 23, taken in the Petworth district, perhaps at Burton in 1939, shows an unfinished kiln, the stack partly covered with coarse grass, and the burner demonstrating how the stake can be pulled out.

The Bewdley Museum Information Sheet "Charcoal Burning in the Wyre Forest" describes a flue built around a central stake, and another account given in papers held by that Museum is of a flue constructed by Mr. Potter, one of the burners consulted, made

21. Kiln at the Open Air Museum at Maria Saal, Austria. The central flue here is
     formed of three uprights held in position by three metal rings.

22. A detail of the central flue seen in Plate 21.

23. A kiln in the Petworth district — possibly at Burton Park — showing the central pole around which it is built, the covering of grass over the wood. The earth for the final covering can be seen on the extreme left and, on the right, a curved ladder. The photograph is dated July 1939.

of forked or hooked staves. Mr. Bond, of the Oxfordshire County Museum, remembers discussing this with Mr. Nevey, a very experienced burner, who confirmed its feasibility; but he did not see such a flue. The sharp ends of the staves were driven into the hearth and the bifurcated tops interlocked — but it is not clear just how.

Mr. Nevey, who conducted the Wyre Forest experimental burn in 1973, built his kiln round six foot stakes driven into the centre of the hearth to form a tripod, with the object of preventing the burning wood with which the kiln is lit falling to the bottom of the stack, the intention being that the fire should burn down the chimney space and out to the edges of the stack. Against this tripod, the wood is set, the heaviest at the inside of the kiln.

Plate 24 is also of Wyre Forest provenance, and shows the nucleus of a kiln. Without documentation one can only assume it is a core intended to prevent the kindling dropping to the foot of the kiln and that the structure of the flue is not yet complete. Two separate photographs show this detail so that it is reasonable to suppose it was integral to these burners' method of kiln building.

In the Furness area, the construction of the kiln is different. Mr. Bill Norris, from whose notes and article, "Filming a Charcoal Burn", in "Cumbria" (March 1973) much of the detail concerning charcoal burning in the Lakeland area given here is drawn, supplied the diagram (Fig. 5) showing a two-tier kiln with a "motty peg flue". Mr. Norris worked with Mr. Jack Allonby in the demonstration burn carried out at Ickenthwaite. In this kind of charcoal pit the bottom tier is built around a thick central pole, the wood leaning inwards a little. Two lengths of wood are used, "shanklings" about three feet long and "coalwood" of two feet. Both are cut obliquely so that they do not make a sealed area where they touch the ground. The shanklings are used for two-thirds of the diameter of the first tier, then the central pole is cut off and replaced with a shorter length, a "motty peg" sometimes with lugs pointed at the end stuck into the centre of the shanklings. (Plate 25). Around this, the coalwood is vertically stacked and it is graded to cover the outer third of the kiln's diameter giving a domed contour over it; horizontally placed thinner wood is added. The diagram shows this clearly. This flue is fired by tipping in previously ignited charcoal.

These different flues may, or may not, have been peculiar to the districts where, until recently they were still used; it is impossible to assert even that the triangular flue, which seems only to be known of in the south of England, and which John Evelyn describes, was "standard" for the south east in the face of such evidence of variety as is given by Plate 18. Evidence which exists may be contradictory; as in Pyne's "Microcosm of Early Trades and Industries"[1] for example, where a flue is being built of horizontally placed cordwood in the drawing while the explanatory text describes a pole centred box type flue.

Accounts of bottom-fired kilns are spoken of by individuals who remember seeing charcoal burning many years ago and from districts as widely separated as Cumbria and Sussex. They are thought to have been ignited through a tunnel left in the base, which could be kept open by the insertion of a stout pole; though it is easy to imagine this might very easily have become trapped by the weight of the wood above it. Mr. F. Holmes (whose diagram of a bloomery is seen in Fig. 1), and who saw this method of kindling when a boy, points out that old time Sussex gardeners used to build what they called "denture" fires kindled from the base in this way. These, he says, were used especially where new ground was being cleared, also to get rid of ground elder, cootch grass, etc. The fires were built to a height of five feet or more, covered with turves, grass side inwards. When the covering was complete, the heap was further covered with ash from previous fires or whatever was at hand to seal it. The fires would burn for up to ten days, gradually reducing themselves till only a pile of fine ash was left. In his recollection, charcoal kilns also built on this principle retained the central pole to give a chimney vent.

Bottom lighting might possibly be illustrated at the bottom left hand corner of Plate 18, where a protruding pole is clearly visible at the base. This might possibly be to make a channel through which tar by-products could be collected while burning was in process, but such an explanation seems improbable for the collection of tar was generally secured by building the kiln over a hard surface, raised above ground level, with a central depression into which the

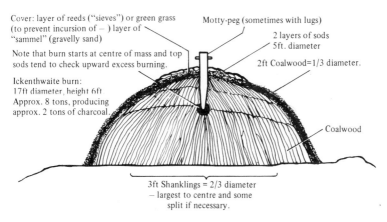

Cover: layer of reeds ("sieves") or green grass
(to prevent incursion of −) layer of
"sammel" (gravelly sand)

Note that burn starts at centre of mass and top
sods tend to check upward excess burning.

Ickenthwaite burn:
17ft diameter, height 6ft
Approx. 8 tons, producing
approx. 2 tons of charcoal.

Motty-peg (sometimes with lugs)

2 layers of sods
5ft. diameter

2ft Coalwood=1/3 diameter.

Coalwood

3ft Shanklings = 2/3 diameter
− largest to centre and some
split if necessary.

5.   Cross section of a Cumbrian kiln, by Mr. A. W. Norris.

24.   Another kiln centre, this time a core to prevent the kindling sinking to the bottom of the heap, the flue of which would be relatively shallow. This kiln was in the Wyre Forest.

25.   This kiln, at Statterthwaite, has a "motty-peg" flue. The central flue reached down only to the top of the first tier of wood, which is packed solid. The chimney is kept open by a short length of stave — the "motty-peg" — and when this is withdrawn burning charcoal is tipped in.

26. Demonstration charcoal encampment set up at Ickenthwaite. The kiln is partly covered and the screens covered with bracken to exclude wind can be seen behind it to the left.

27. Charcoal burners lighting up in the Forest of Dean. The basket, which would hold sifted soil, is light to handle.

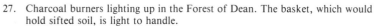

liquid could collect and from which it might be run. Or, it may be simply a vent hole, as in Plate 20. Plate 16 shows the beginning of an African kiln, which was fired at the base, a hole being kept for this purpose in the narrow side.

Unfortunately, Mr. Morewood Dowsett does not describe the central flue found in the rectangular kilns seen in Sweden. Further, in his article he writes, but again without elaboration, that a kiln may be fired by a method involving a horizontal gallery, firing being effected from the side, or both from the top and sides. As he says that the most common method would seem to be the erection of cone shaped piles of billets about twelve feet high, with a diameter of twelve to forty feet, one might think the stacks in Plates 17 and 18 could be related but these reveal no such method of side firing. These kilns are certainly, by ordinary standards, so unusual as to seem incredible. It is much to be regretted that there appears to be no further bibliographical record.

Whichever the flue, the cordwood is built around it, whether of greenwood or seasoned wood will affect the length of time taken to char it, and the yield, but they can be mixed, provided that wood with a rotted core (sometimes called a "glede", a "dolted core") is not included — such could channel a draught when the kiln is opened after cooling and start a flare-up. Wood up to seven inches diameter can be charred in the round; thicker wood is split to ensure even burning. It may be stripped of its bark or not. When oak bark was required by tanners, this was, of course, taken, the wood being cut in the late spring and early summer when bark could be most easily removed. When all is in place, including the domed uppermost tier, the whole is covered with a layer of thinner sticks, between one inch and two in thickness, to cover the fissures between staves where the air might too easily penetrate. (Plate 13). Vegetation is now spread over the stack leaving the chimney vent free and this is well damped so that the outermost covering of earth shall adhere to it.

Here is another point of divergence. Many burners cover (or are reported to have covered), with turf. Others used only a fine dust of riddled earth and the sandy residue, carefully saved for repeated re-use from previous burnings. Mr. Frank Holmes reports clay having been used in the Weald of Sussex — it might well have been all there was to use.

Mr. and Mrs. Langridge used, and say Mr. Francis used also, sand, finely riddled earth and dust from former burnings, which they say "was like gold dust to us, it was our stock in trade". When they moved to another site they took it with them in sacks. The use of turf, they claim, would produce a dirty crop, lumps of earth mixing with the charcoal which would not pass through the riddle.

The vegetation under the earth might be straw, reeds, bracken, grass, weeds and the mixed rakings from the hearth site if a new one were used. In the Wyre Forest, this process is called "shingling" the clamp, and at this stage, Mr. Nevey put a sack into the chimney hole to keep it clear of dirt. The outer cover is patted onto the damped vegetation and made firm and even. In the Furness Fells, this layer is called "sammel" — taken from a subsoil half-way between gravelly sand and clay; over it a circular mat of turves is placed about five feet wide and two turves deep, with the grass sides together to keep in the top heat. Plate 26 (showing the same hut at Ickenthwaite as that in Plate 9) also shows a kiln which has been left partly uncovered to reveal the stages of construction. In the background are the lews, hung with bracken. In all cases, water must be accessible, brought in a cart if there is no stream and put ready in buckets or barrels. A hundred gallons is more than is required but it is quicker to fill a bucket from a half full barrel than an empty one as the water is used up and a reserve is necessary against a flare-up.

The motty peg, or central stake, being drawn out (and any sacking removed) kindling begins, using either wood or charcoal. If the former, brands imperfectly charred from the previous burn, with other short lengths of wood, are made into a bonfire and when burning well are tipped into the flue. If charcoal is preferred (as in the Ickenthwaite burn), it is made hot and glowing. Periodically, more wood taken from the short pieces set aside is added until the flue is quite filled up with burning core (Plates 27 & 28). Between stokings, which may take place at two-hour intervals or more frequently, the chimney is blocked with vegetation and sand, turf, or, in the Wyre Forest tradition, with a flat, circular metal cover called a plate. This stoking is known as "dressing the stack". Mr. Nevey's clamp of three and a half cords continued to be so dressed into the day following the kindling. The kilns at the Weald and Downland Open Air Museum, at Singleton — of about three cords — were dressed more frequently over a shorter period of time, the entire burning taking little more than twenty-four hours.

When the initial fuelling is completed, the top is finally sealed; the plate is discarded (if it has been used) and the flue covered either, as in Cumbria, with a mat of turf (Plate 29) or elsewhere with the same materials as the rest of the kiln. The charcoal burner now regulates the air supply to the kiln by making small holes with the handle of one of his tools, a rauber or firgun stick. Again, accounts vary from a firm statement of procedure to the pragmatic. Of the former, these vent holes are made first near the top of the kiln, then, as the kiln burns, they are stopped and a new series lower down commenced until the bottom is reached. A photograph by Toni Schneiders of a large kiln in Sweden[2] shows a very regular series of vent holes smoking at the base of a kiln which, judging by its shape, seems to be nearing completion of burning. In the Wyre Forest account, Mr. Nevey steered the course of burning by making vent holes as the emission of smoke from the stack indicated the need. Mrs. Langridge says that "to make the kiln burn evenly all

28. The kiln (at the Weald and Downland Open Air Museum) has been fed with burning embers. The smoke from these rises through the open flue and small billets of wood taken up in a sack are being fed into it — a process called "dressing the stack".

29. In Cumbria the kiln, when it is burning, is sealed with a circular "mat" of turves placed over the top.

30. Smoking kiln at the Weald & Downland Museum, 1972.

31. A smoking kiln with charcoal burners. The date of the photograph is about 1890 and the camera focus gives a surprising diminution in size between the figure in the foreground and those in the middle distance. The screens set up here are very high and extensive.

round, small holes are made about half way down from the shoulder of the fire, but this is only done if it is burning on one side more than the other, or, if the fire is burning too slowly. We also make holes right on the hearth at the bottom to burn the ends, which we call footends". Making holes at the bottom lets out any sap from the wood (or tar products). "We only make holes at the bottom when the rest of the fire is burnt out; as soon as the fire is burnt far enough the holes are closed".

Mr. Allonby points out that "Everything you have to work with can be different — the soil cover and the ground can be different. In one part of the country the soil can be very close, almost like clay . . . hence the 'pricking'. Here, in Cumbria, once the soil has been put on there is practically no need to touch it but you have to know how much soil to put on. There are around here hundreds of acres of peat moss . . . with a vast amount of wood growing on them. All this at one time was cut and made into charcoal. There you have nothing at all in the way of soil, so this wood had to be carted to the soil, or the soil carted to the wood. Again, if you were going to coal the wood on peat-moss ground, you had to do something before you set the wood out on it. The wood would burn all right but the fire would not stop when it got to the bottom of the pit. It would carry on into the peat . . . So, sea sand was carried from the shore and spread four to six inches thick on the pit bottom". The smoke should issue from the pores of the covering and should be even all round (Plate 30). Screens of metal, hessian, wooden frames interlaced with bracken or banks of brushwood (Plate 31), sometimes called "lews" — an obsolete word meaning shelter — are set round the kiln to protect it from the wind (Plates 26, 29, 33 & 34).

Plate 17 shows screens of stakes. While a kiln is burning another can be built (Plate 32).

The time taken for burning may be from two days to ten and not necessarily in proportion to the size of the kiln. The degree of seasoning of the wood, the ventilation and the efficiency of the kindling, play their parts. A very small experimental kiln of five and a half hundredweight of coppice, burned by the Wheelwright Archaeological Society of Dewsbury, required six and a half days to burn and produced the correct amount of charcoal. A larger stack of six tons may be converted in four and a half days. Burners say "from five to ten days" for a working sized stack. The Ickenthwaite stack (Plate 26) charred in three days.

The temperature within the kiln is variable. A very quick burn with relatively more air will cause a greater shrinkage of wood than a slow one. The charcoal yield from retort factories mainly concerned with the extraction of by-products is proportionately less than by the older, slower processes..

The temperature given for charcoal production is 500°C. and 600°C. by Chambers' Encyclopaedia and by McGraw-Hill's "Encyclopaedia of Technology", respectively. For special pur-

32. This photograph, taken in 1952, shows earth covered kilns still being burned in Kent; this was not a "demonstration" burn.

33. Raking the pit, Wyre Forest. This is a preparatory stage in the cooling and opening of the kiln. The portable metal screens are characteristic of the locality.

poses, temperatures are higher than this and it may be assumed that these figures are based on modern, highly controlled techniques.

During the burning — the word is misleading for charring is more akin to baking than to burning, no flame being produced — the damp and tars from the wood darken the cover, which dries out during the burning, the dark band diminishing towards the base. It is not unknown for the gases driven off to cause an explosion within the kiln blowing it open. While charring the wood shrinks and loses half, perhaps two-thirds, of its original volume. The dirt covering may crack or fall in here and there, the kiln may even twist and make a bigger gap in the surface; the burner must constantly be aware of any hole through which the heap might receive enough oxygen to start a flare up, and subsequent bonfire. For this reason, nocturnal watch is kept and even experienced men tell of occasions when they "dozed off" with disastrous results. Ordinarily, cracks or gaps are quickly damped and filled with more cover.

John Evelyn says that the stack, when the "dense and thick clouds" of smoke have become more "blue and livid", will cool itself (the vents being stopped). This is in fact done with modern metal kilns but, with earth-burned kilns, it is usual to quench the stack with water. Mr. Norris considers that blue smoke betokens too much burning, too fast. Properly controlled, the grey smoke is gone and there is a shimmer of heat over the heap, a sign that the charcoal is ready for cooling. Sections of the dirt covering are removed with a rake or rauber (Plates 33 and more fancifully, 34), first going round the top half of the kiln section by section, damping the wood below and covering it again with fresh unheated dust kept for the purpose, and then, doing the same one part after another, round the lower half of the kiln. In Cumbria, this damping of the pit is called "flaying", and the spraying of water is done, Mr. Allonby says, by throwing water from a ladle with a special twist of the wrist. When all is covered again, the ladder is put against the stack and the burner goes up with water and a "firgun" stick. With the point, he makes a hole in the top of the kiln and dribbles water into it down the handle, then makes more such holes and introduces water into them. At first, this must be done carefully and slowly for a sudden flow of water into an open hole would result in a dangerous jet of steam. Fifty gallons of water might be used to quench a seven cord kiln. This does not extinguish the wood by direct contact but the steam will effect the quenching in all parts of the stack, especially as now all the holes are blocked and no air admitted. Usually a few hours pass before it is judged wise to open the kiln and begin to sort the crop.

When the kiln is taken apart (which is called "drawing the pit" or "drawing the stack") (Plate 35), the dirt covering is carefully raked off and set aside for further use. Beneath it, the charcoal, although shrunken from the size of the wood stack, should preserve its shape and natural markings and not be broken much. It is

34. An artist's interpretation of charcoal burning. The tool over the shoulder of the man in the background is rather indeterminate, being too small for a rake. Otherwise, except for the absence of the usual working mess, it would seem to have been correctly observed.

claimed that even the form of a bracken spray may be preserved. If a small bunch of willow twigs has been included — as were used to make artists' pencils — they should be intact and removed before the taking apart of the heavier coals endangers them. The charcoal will be silvery-black, clean looking and glossy, giving a light ringing sound if two pieces strike together.

The coals are sorted and the dust which has fallen into the kiln is riddled out (Plate 36). Any unburnt stumps from the outside bottom of the heap are put aside to be used as kindling later. Care must be taken that the fire does not "come back to life". A light wind can be dangerous, splashing with water is a safeguard but it is important the crop should not be overdamped — damp charcoal is not only a poor fuel but a potentially dangerous one, as, if it burns, it produces carbon-monoxide fumes. Water can be splashed with the hands, or a spray of leafy twigs used. After the cleaning, the sorting and the cooling is finished the charcoal is tipped into sacks with a specially curved rib-shovel and is ready to be taken away (Plate 37). For the burners, the work cycle is completed here. The burners might cut and burn, or burn only, following the wood-cutters. Mr. Langridge, when he was "working on his own", did both cutting and burning. Mr. Francis was exclusively a burner and did not cut; going to areas where the wood had already been stacked, useful brushwood left in heaps, and the waste disposed of in bonfires. For making huts for shelter, he might take the leaning side growths from coppice, but never straight oak. Hazel could be cut from the hedges for the outer covering layer of wood if this was necessary. The wood for the kilns might come from the larger trees, the tops and branches, for which the timber merchant had no use, or from coppice wood.

"Lop and top", the name sometimes given to the upper branches of forest trees also means wood from trees pollarded to grow branches for fuel when timber was scarce. Even large-growing trees, such as beech and hornbeam can be so used, and the well-known Burnham Beeches are trees that were pollarded from about 1500 to 1820.[3]

Mr. Langridge said that after the weekend's lull, charcoal burners frequently felt sickened by the fumes given off when the next kiln was kindled. Mr. Harber, on the other[4] hand, told that his predecessor worked until he was eighty-seven years old, without a day's illness until a week or so before he died.

The wood used for charcoal making can be of almost any kind; some is suitable for the production of charcoal for particular purposes. John Evelyn tells us that alder — and limetree wood, if available — makes the best charcoal for gun-powder making and to these may be added the alder-buckthorn (Rhannus frangula, sometimes called the berry-bearing alder, although not of the alder family) and the willow. Beech and birch are best for charcoal used in the manufacture of carbon disulphide, required by the artificial

35. These burners at Ambleside are dismantling a kiln. The outer crust is being raked away with a corrack (a tool which has a board, toothed on one side only, as its head). The big tubs are to hold water.

36. Mr. and Mrs. Langridge at the Weald & Downland Museum sorting "the crop" after a burn, and riddling away the dust.

silk industry and for this last, oak is unsuitable. Willow twigs produce a soft charcoal, which was liked for artists' pencils. Ash and hornbeam are acceptable, conifers and chestnut are light and break easily but old hop poles, often of chestnut, are a recognised material for the burners. Elm is not liked as it gives a poor yield; but the only wood against which Mr. and Mrs. Langridge discriminate is the elder, which, they say, always causes trouble if it is included in a kiln. This tree, which seldom reaches a size that would make it seem worthy of consideration, seems to have been generally an object of superstitious dislike; there is a saying in Needwood Forest (north of Leicester) that "To burn elder would raise the Devil". Woodcutters used to exclude it from their fires when they were burning waste.[5]

The tools used in charcoal burning are various and have been subject to addition and adaptation by individual burners although one supposes that when the industry flourished they may have been more "standardised". Reference has already been made to a rib shovel (Plate 38). The rabil, rubler or rauber is also called a rebel, a cooler or a wiper. The wiper used by Mr. Langridge in the Singleton Museum demonstrations was an oblong piece of wood fixed to a long pole. Its use was for removing the sand when the burning was complete. The other end of the handle was sharpened for making the necessary ventilation holes as required in the finished heap. Mr. Nevey, in the Wyre Forest[6] used a "raugle" as a wiper, which was half-moon shaped, and the pointed end of the pole he called a "Firgun stick" though the Langridges had no name for it. This pointed end is, in some other cases, encased in metal and may go by the name of a "Furgey stick". The rib shovel is only mentioned among the tools of Mr. and Mrs. Langridge, who also had a "duster" of birch twigs mounted on a long handle — in the manner of a besom — used for lightly touching away any small stones or other unsuitable material from the surface of the heap which might cause a disturbance while the burn was taking place. The sand easily rolls off and irregularities help to produce an avalanche effect. For the rest, they used shop-bought shovels and buckets. The Museum at Singleton has an authentic charcoal burner's barrow, although the one exhibited on the open site is a replica. It is a long skeleton barrow, sometimes called a "mare", and is here shown in the frontispiece illustration. Its open sides are suited to the carrying of lengths of wood. Its use was not confined to the Weald — Bewdley Museum also has one painted according to tradition, blue with red wheels — and they have another carrier, a wheel-less stretcher suitable for the carrying of charcoal.

The screens which Mr. Allonby made were frames consisting of two side pieces, eight feet long with five lighter cross members and he called them hurdles. The interstices were filled with bracken and the whole screen — or, rather, screens, for there must be enough to surround the hearth — supported by props leaning

37. Using a rib-shovel to tip charcoal into a sack.

against them (Plate 26). In the Wyre Forest, metal sheets (Plate 33) with pointed protruding feet to spike in the ground were used: hessian was tied between poles at Singleton.

Less hazardous than the notched tiller (a tiller is the name given to sapling trunks grown from coppice) of which John Evelyn writes is a ladder made from two curved saplings with cross pieces, fitted to the shape of the kiln. (Plates 23, 38 & 46).

Other charcoal burners' tools include a corrack, which in the equipment of Mr. Frank Harber, was called a "cowrake" and was a board toothed on one side on a handle, but it is reported as being simply a rake, with long teeth, in Wyre. Mr. Norris reports that, in Cumbria, a corrack or cowrake is called a "cooler" (Fig. 6) and is a board on a handle such as is sometimes called a rauber or rauble in other districts. The toothed tool he calls a sod rake or a drag rake. The continuance of a name but difference in the tool to which it is applied suggests a fragmented tradition. Miss Hartley[7] shows a long toothed rake with four prongs called a graip. A long-handled shovel — in the Wyre Forest equipment called a ship — had a curved eight foot handle and a heart shaped or curved edged steel blade. The staff shovel illustrated in Miss Hartley's book, is a spade shaped tool, the handle of which curves at the lower end and joins the blade in the middle of its back. She also shows a branchlet of spruce with which water could be sprinkled. Sometimes, wooden bowls painted white for visibility in semi-darkness were used; floating on a barrel of water these could quickly be seized in an emergency. A stocker — an adze-like implement for clearing the site of a hearth (a kiln on a newly prepared site in Wyre was called "a green one") — is to be seen in Plate 18 being used by the figure in the foreground to the left. Baskets, or cauls, might be included, sacks were required supplied by the iron works or marketers (and useful for lining a hut or hanging as a curtain in a doorway).

The charcoal produced by Mr. Allonby's Ickenthwaite burn was packed into sacks measuring five feet by two.

6a.

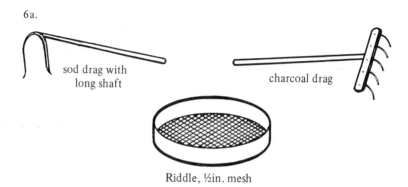

sod drag with
long shaft

charcoal drag

Riddle, ½in. mesh

Sack holder

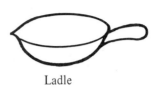

Ladle

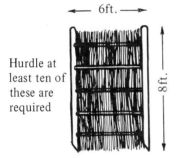

Hurdle at least ten of these are required

Barrel, 18 gallons, Three of these are required

Pick

Spade

6. & 7.   Mr. J. Allonby's tools.

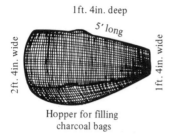

1ft. 4in. deep

5' long

2ft. 4in. wide

1ft. 4in. wide

Hopper for filling
charcoal bags

Bearing Swill for
carrying soil approx.
12 gallons.

Water tub for stangs

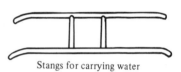

Stangs for carrying water

Cooler for pulling down soil
when cooling.
One with long shaft and one
short.

Turf spade for cutting sods

Shool for working on the burning pit
one with long shaft and one with short

After diagrams by Mr. J. Allonby

In the Wyre Forest, a plate is used to close the flue of the clamp between dressings. Barrels of water are also needed. In the Furness area, a hearth is called a "pit-stead"[8] and the kiln is a "pit". In Sussex, a pit is, we are told,[9] pronounced "pet" and it is "set" upon a hearth. Mrs. Langridge, however, says she has never known the word pit so used, what her family burned was an "earth burned fire".

Mr. Allonby has provided drawings of a number of tools which he is familiar with — except for the riddle, the cooler being the only one identical with Mr. Langridge's and by him called a wiper. (Figs. 6 & 7). Early illustrations sometimes show a high-sided cart for carrying away the charcoal.

A singular piece of equipment not so far, it would seem, mentioned elsewhere is reported by Mr. Morewood Dowsett as sometimes being used: a portable hood of wood, coated with loam and vegetation for covering the heap and protected from the intense heat of the kiln by packings of dry charcoal dust. It is not at all easy to imagine this although it may have been an experimental forerunner of the metal kilns with which we are familiar today.

Of an earlier date were "banisters", large hampers wider at the top than the bottom and with the bottom removable for tipping. These could be carried on either side of a horse. As, because of the shape, they could also be hollow-filled, they permitted cheating and were, during the eighteenth century, given up in favour of sacks.[10]

38. Charcoal burning, c. 1890. In the smoke a man can be seen on top of the kiln. A curved ladder is below and supports for screens are all round, although it is only on the windward side they have been used to support faggots.

THE YIELD AND ITS VALUE

It is difficult to arrive at a meaningful scale of quantities. Wood differs greatly in weight from the heavy oak to the softwoods and again moisture content affects weights: it may be as low as 10 per cent or as high as 70 per cent gross, and this is driven off in the charring. One cannot assume that seasoned timber was the rule — one Agreement for the burning of coppice states, as a condition, that the burning should take place as soon as possible after cutting.[1] From light wood, light charcoal results so one load may be very different in weight from another. For convenience, one may assume that the weight of wood in relation to the charcoal it produces may be 7:1 or 5:1. If five to one is taken as a proportion, a cord of wood weighing about 25 cwt (again an arbitrary figure) will yield a quarter of a ton of charcoal.

W. R. Butterfield states that a cord yields forty bushels of coals: H. L. Edlin says thirty bushels and, in "Tudor Food and Pastimes" by F. G. Emmison, we learn that in the middle of the sixteenth century a sack of charcoal had to contain four bushels but that a century later, a load is stated to have been 30 sacks of three bushels.

Nor can one easily find comparisons by which a collier's prosperity might be measured during the last five centuries; to do so, one would need in every case to know the price initially paid for cordwood to the woodcutters and to the carriers.

The following values are drawn from Ernest Straker's "Wealden Iron":

1539   Coals delivered to furnace at Newbridge 3/- per load.

1546   Wood cutting 3d. per cord, Coaling 12½d per load — no figure being given for cordwood at Penningridge.

1639—

1755   Wood bought standing, per cord, 6/-, cutting 1/1d to 1/3d per cord; coaling 2/6d and 2/8¾d per load at Heathfield.

1757—

1792   Wood bought standing, 10/6d—13/8d per cord, cutting 1/3d—2/1d, Coaling 2/6d—2/8d per load.

In "Archives and Local History", F. G. Emmison gives an Account from the ironworks at Cannock Chase in 1578, where the colliers were paid for "colinge" seventeen loads of coal, 22/6d. The carriage on thirty-five loads of coals was 23/4d. Mr. Emmison, in "Tudor Foods and Pastimes", quotes another account, dated 1546, in which 35/5d is the sum paid for seven loads of charcoal, burned by "my master's collier in Essex". This is a relatively high price — but, the same man, Petre of Ingatestone Hall, paid 24/9d for a further load and sixteen sacks of charcoal bought in "from outside" at about the same time.

For the interest of comparison, during the fourteenth century, smiths who were paid a price "per bloom" received, in addition, beer money to the sum of 1d. per week, to be divided between four men. In the sixteenth century, the iron workers' wages were between eight and nine shillings and sixpence per week for founders, four and six shillings for fillers: and in the middle of the eighteenth century, founders were earning ten shillings and fillers seven or eight shillings per week.[3]

Not only are weights and measures difficult to correlate, but during all this time the value of money changed with an uneven but continuous inflation. It appears to be substantiated, however, that the price of charcoal was always a considerable charge and could be as high as sixty per cent of the total cost of iron production.

Mr. A. B. Bartlett, the Archivist to the Beaulieu Estate, has drawn up an account of the ironworks at Sowley, in the south-west corner of the Manor of Beaulieu, which affords some information concerning charcoal and the wood from which it is made, in relation to one ironworks over a century and a half. Mr. Bartlett has kindly given permission for the use of these notes.

The ironworks were set up by about 1600; there is no evidence of the exact date but in 1605 a complaint was made at Southampton Court Leet, that the newly erected ironworks at Beaulieu and Tychfield "ingrosse the woods and underwoods there abouts which were formerley vented to this place". The reference to Tychfield is to a forge there; the furnace being at Bewley. When a list had been taken by appraisers in 1601 — following the sentencing of the Third Earl of Southampton, the then owner of the estate, for his part in the Essex Rising — quantities of wood were among the items and the price for 571 cords was £280.11s.0d. Records show that 2,642 cordes of wood were employed to the Sowley ironworks during the year 1606/7.

In 1699, the Titchfield forge having become separated from the Sowley furnace and works, a new forge was proposed to be built at Sowley: the lessee representing that the cost could be met by the sale of timber and recovered in rents, also that the scheme would provide a market for all the coppice wood of the estate.

In 1716, a paper among the estate documents, headed "Querys and Remarks" was drawn up raising questions and giving some estimates of cost. One of the queries is "How much coale 100 Acres of coppice might reasonably yield?" and it is remarked that "3 cole fires on an acre one so by another each cole fire makes 1½ loads of charcole. An estimate for Annual stock includes:

700 Loads of coals for 30 foundings at 3¼ to a ton of pig iron.	£700.00.00
500 Tons of Oar at 7s. first cost, watter and land carriage 3s.	250.00.00
Rent of Mills and repairs.	60.00.00

which, since the 30 foundings are estimated, in the account of the annual product, to be worth £1,260 shows that the fuel was responsible for a very high proportion of the costing. The foundrymen and the clerk (or manager) together earned £85.''

Here we find a new term, a "coalfire", and in a new lease of the ironworks, in 1717, it appears again as a standard of measurement. The Duke is to be responsible for the cutting of coppice and undergrowth of fifteen years' growth each year and having it made into "coalfires". Each coalfire is to be 33 feet on the ground, 4½ feet high and 2 feet 8 inches in breadth. (About two cords of wood). The coal fires are to be burnt into coals as soon as convenient after felling at places in the wood where they will do no damage to growing timber: the price to the tenant is 20/-d. per coalfire, plus 1/- poundage to the Steward. There is an inflation-pegged clause that prices may rise but not above 24/- per coalfire during the 15-year lease. The wood for cabins (presumably for the burners to shelter in) is to be supplied by the Duke at the rate of 10s. for every hundred coalfires. These coalfires were small — obviously not expected to yield 1½ loads of charcoal each.

The computation of the cost of charcoal for an average year, between 1718 and 1721, was £500, which by the reckoning points to an output of pig iron of 230 tons.

In 1752, an air furnace, or Reverberatory furnace, was set up at Sowley, which was charcoal fuelled. It consisted of two compartments, one for the fuel and one for the metal, separated by a bridge. The heat was deflected or "reverberated" by the slope of the roof on to the iron.

In 1763, a new lessee was William Ford (of Grizedale) and one finds comparisons of prices in Sowley and Lancashire:

In Lancashire . . 1 charcoal at 38s.	£3.	9. 8
1¾ ore at 14s.	£1.	4. 6
	£4.14.	2
At Sowley . . . . . 1¾ ore at 27s.	£2.	7. 3
2 charcoal at 23/5½	£2.	6.11
	£4.14.	2

The ore may have been of a different quality, or may have had a high cost for carriage, or both. The difference in the cost of charcoal can only be attributed to the collapse of the once flourishing markets in the south.

In a survey of 1767, Thomas Browne, the surveyor, stated that the availability of cheap fuel from the woods could be the only reason for maintaining ironworks in such a place, so distant from large towns and having to rely on ore brought from Lancashire and other places.

In 1772, we have vouchers which give the cost of burning and carrying as follows:

Burning ...... 304 loads of charcoal, the produce
        of 325 tons, four fathom of wood
        upon Beaulieu Manor.   £77.10.00
Carrying ...... 304 loads of charcoal to
        Sowley works.   £74.16.06

The ironworks at Sowley declined in productivity during the latter part of the eighteenth century. They did not function at all between 1769 and 1790, and came to an end when in 1822 the forge closed down.

From the Lancashire district, Articles of Agreement between Wm. Penny and Partners[4] (about to set up an ironworks on the River Crake), and several persons (colliers) made provision that the agreement was to cover 30 years, the Penny partnership having the right to terminate it at eight months' notice at any time if they found the trade in iron became unprofitable. They were to have the monopoly of charcoal made by the "several persons" after a given date, before which time outstanding orders could be filled by the latter and they would pay for charcoal delivered each year, before Midsummer Day at or upon the 1st August, following, or for that delivered before Martinmas (11th November) at or upon the 2nd February.

The price fixed was 34/-d. for every load of a dozen sacks, and in proportion for a load of lesser quantity, delivered to the intended ironworks on the River Crake; but, if works were built along another river, then twelve pence per dozen sacks, per mile, would be paid to meet the cost of transport.

A proviso was added to peg the cost to that of iron. If the then current price of pig iron at Bristol were to rise or fall, 1/- per dozen should be added or abated on every 5/- a ton in advance or fall of iron.

For preventing any dispute about measure of coals, it was agreed that the sacks should be supplied by Wm. Penny in a sufficient quantity to meet requirements and, when delivered, the coals "fairly set down" should stand 4 feet 9 inches high in a sack "only one yard between seam and seam". If any complaints arose about measure, three days' notice would be given during which time the collier or carrier might make up the sacks to a reasonable quantity without removing any, otherwise, compensation must be made.

More recent prices show surprising fluctuations: Mr. Allonby learned from a charcoal burner working in the Forest of Dean that, during the years 1905-6, he was selling charcoal at £4.0.0d. a ton. Mr. Allonby's father's Day Book, for those years, shows that fifteen tons were delivered by him to the Backbarrow forge for £10.0.0d. a ton.

Mr. and Mrs. Langridge say that around 1914, the price paid to Mr. Francis by the fuel dealer for whom he worked was £1.10.0d. or £2.0.0d. a load. This does not offer a very satisfactory comparison as it was for the burning only, not for the wood, or the preparation of the wood, nor for the marketing. The Bewdley Museum information sheet states that during the inter-war years, charcoal sold at prices between £2.10.0d. and £10.10.0d. per ton.

Mr. Kelley, of Messrs. Shirley Aldred and Co., writes that retort charcoal (destined for gunpowder) was quoted at 22s.9d. per cwt in 1801 (a very high price). In 1919, his company sold charcoal for between £8 and £9 per ton.

In 1938, W. R. Butterfield reported that the price of charcoal had dropped from 9d. to 4d. per bushel and a reader's letter in the same journal for the following month, drew attention to an account dated 28th August, 1937, as follows:

Charcoal burning for Capt. Budd (of Ladysden).
(Burning) 13 cord of cordwood at 9s. per cord.   £5.17.0
Hearth money.   4.0
    Received with thanks.
    Thomas Manktelow, Marden, Kent.
(bearing a George VI Coronation stamp).

The same charcoal was sold at 10d. per bushel. Hearth money means beer money.

By 1941, the price to the fuel merchant was about £11 a ton. The Forest Record[5] gives prices for 1960 as follows:

Lump: £22-£30 per ton, delivered.
Granulated: £26-£40 per ton, delivered.
Chalm (powdered dust): £10 per ton upwards depending on
                       size and quantity.

These are, of course, fuel merchants' prices, as also are those for 1976:[6]

Barbecue Charcoal — packs of approximately 20 lbs.
1- 9 packs .... £2.00 each.
10 packs .... £1.60 each.
25 packs .... £1.50 each.
50 packs .... £1.25 each.
which amounts to £140 per ton.

Messrs. Shirley Aldred quote their 1977 prices as from £90-£100 for low grade and £140 for top quality material, these prices being for bulk buying.

NEW TIMES, NEW METHODS

The industrial revolution did not altogether leave the charcoal burning industry undisturbed. In "A General View of the Agriculture of the County of Sussex", by the Rev. Arthur Young, first published in 1808, one reads of modernization.

"The manufacture of charcoal is an object of some consequence in such a county as Sussex. Large quantities are annually sent to London by land carriage. The old process in burning has been lately laid aside and a new method substituted . . .

Adjoining the turnpike at North Chapel and within five miles of Petworth, Government has lately purchased a small piece of land of Lord Egremont and upon it have erected this charcoal manufactory. The cylinder room is 60 feet in length, and proportionately high and wide: three sets of iron cylinders are placed in a very thick wall, or bed of brick-work, built nearly along the centre of the house. Each of them contains three cylinders, each being six feet long and two feet in diameter. To prevent every possibility of air being admitted, iron stops are contrived, 18 inches in length and the size of the inner circumference of the cylinder, which are placed in the mouth and are filled and rammed down with sand. Besides which, sand-doors (as they call them) are made to project obliquely over the front or opening of the cylinder and are entirely filled with sand and the stops covered with it. At the back part of the building, are copper pipes projecting seven feet in length, communicating at one extremity with the far end of the cylinder, at the other extremity immersed in half-hogshead barrels. These pipes serve to draw off the steam or liquid, which flows in large quantities into the tar barrels during the process of charring. Sea coal fires are made under them, one to each set; in order to convey the heat as equally as possible to all parts of the cylinders alike, four flues or cavities equidistant from each other in the brick work, spirally encircle the cylinders and conduct the heat over every part. The position of the grate was, at first, over the central cylinder. Various alterations have since been made as it was found that this method did not answer as how to heat all the cylinders equally. The grate is now placed under the outside cylinder in each of the sets; and by the flues being so conveyed it follows that the further cylinder is first heated, that which is nearest the fire the last. Each set holds 5 cwt of wood so that when all three are in full work, the daily consumption is 15 cwt of wood, which makes 4 cwt of coal. It loses nearly three parts out of four in charring and, if all the three sets were in constant work, the annual consumption would be nearly 550,000 cwt — 27,500 ton.

The process of this novel and valuable operation may be thus explained. Very early in the morning, the first thing to be done by the workmen is to take the doors down by a pulley suspended at the ceiling, remove the sand, also take the sand out of the stops previous to being drawn out and suspende'd. Large tin coolers are then brought up to the mouth of the cylinder and the charcoal of the preceding day is then drawn with a rake into the cooler and shut up close. As soon as the cylinders are emptied, the workmen are employed in recharging them. For the purpose, the sorts of wood are various but withy and elder are the best. The cordwood is about 18 inches long but before it is placed in the furnace, they cut it into five lengths and all the black knots are cut away. In the act of filling, the largest pieces are placed in the centre and the smaller adjoining the rim. When it is charged, the iron stop is let down by the pulley, put into its place and the sand rammed into the front. The doors are then hung over the mouth and filled up with sand, the fire is kindled and fed until the wood is completely charred, which is known by the tar ceasing to flow through the copper pipes. If the fire is lit about half after six o'clock in the morning, it will take from two to two and a half hours before the wood is at all heated and the liquid begins to flow. At this, the fumes become extremely offensive and, soon after, almost intolerable to any but the workmen. The time required is eight hours but this depends upon the size of the wood. During the operation, attention is paid to the pipes which are inspected lest any air might be accidentally admitted, which would infallibly stop the pipes from working. The first are kept up as strong and bright as is possible; although the waste of sea-coal is not considerable — about eight bushels to each set daily. When the wood ceases to work and the tar to flow, the fire is gradually extinguished which concludes the day's work. The furnaces remaining in the same state until the next morning in order to give them time to cool; when drawn they are replenished in the manner before-mentioned but are always cleaned each day and the pipes once a month.

The wood for this manufactory comes out of the neighbourhood and is bought in at 24s. per stack (fell, flaw and stack), beside the carriage. Large quantities of wood are kept in the yard and stand about a year before using. The stack is here twelve feet long, three feet ten inches high and three feet six inches over, from each is extracted about 55 gallons of tar-liquor . . . at present it cannot be used because a patent is out for the monopoly of its sale. It is worth 6d. per gallon.''

This describes the making of a special charcoal for use as an ingredient in gunpowder and one wonders whether the inclusion of "elder" may be in error for "alder". Mr. Kelley, Managing Director of the charcoal making firm of Shirley Aldred, has supplied notes on the making of gunpowder charcoal, which, he says, is produced at temperatures between 500°F. and 600°F. (260°C.-315°C.) for sporting powder, the "black kinds" being obtained at a higher temperature — "such as 819°F. (437°C.) or so being reserved for military or mining requirements". In Muspratts day, it was found that the first type would ignite spontaneously around 680°F. (360°C.) and he postulates this as the cause of explosions in powder mills. This seems to be correct since those materials if fresh from the kilns would be high in retained volatiles and with the presentation of surface area caused in the grinding process would absorb oxygen quickly, with consequent heating, apart from the heat naturally generated on grinding. Since the three main ingredients of manufacture were and still are ground together, the manufacture must have been a very hazardous occupation . . . "the type of wood was of greater importance before retorts gave closer control of the process: hardwoods were never used, for obvious reasons".

Plate 39 shows two views of the retorts in the gunpowder factory at Faversham to which the Petworth charcoal was sent. They were taken from an MS by John Ticking, Master worker at the Royal Faversham Mills, in 1798. Mr. Morewood Dowsett, in the article quoted from the National Geographical Magazine, writing of gunpowder making, comments that after cooling, the charcoal was stored for about a fortnight before grinding, to lessen the danger of spontaneous combustion.

Not only for gunpowder charcoal was the retort factory productive. Macintosh set up a wood distillation plant in Scotland using seven hundred tons of small wood a year in the making of pyroligneous acid (commercially valuable), while supplying charcoal to the furnaces of Cumberland. The woodlands in this area never recovered.

Further technical advance in charcoal making lies outside the scope of this monograph but, in 1960, the Forestry Commission Report No. 16[1] gave details and photographs of permanently sited retorts and the complex kind of installation needed in a modern wood distillation plant.

However, charcoal is still made in the woodlands in kilns but not under a covering of earth.

Metal kilns were found to give the right condition for burning. Plates 40, 41 and 42 show a form of these, which was used by the Sussex Charcoal Burning Company at Singleton (near the Open Air Museum) in 1938. The metal flue cage is interesting and may be considered as a "survival", for later metal kilns do not incorporate it. These kilns, being moved by pulleys from a scaffolding, are suitable for repeated use in a fixed area, supplies of wood being brought to the kilns. The circular inner cage held the wood —or the charcoal — in place, while the kiln cover was put on or removed. The pipe chimneys, which can be seen smoking in Plate 41 were fixed in holes at the base, one of which is visible in Plate 42.

It has been supposed that the metal kilns were introduced when the need for charcoal revived with the threat of war and its outbreak in 1938 and 1939. The Sussex Magazine carried articles such as "War revives an ancient Craft" (H. E. Hinkley) and "Country Folk make this War Weapon" during the early 'forties. The inference was that the charcoal was required for the filters of gasmasks or for the making of explosives. Whether the "revival" was actually conditioned in this way is problematical. Gas mask filter charcoal is best made from coconut shell at a temperature of 900 degrees, an operation best carried out under controlled conditions. It may be that after 1938, when gas masks were issued to all civilians, and coconut shell would not be easily obtained, some hardwood substitute was found, processed in the country, and further processes, requiring very high temperatures, carried out elsewhere.

39. Two drawings of retorts at a gunpowder factory at Faversham, Kent, at the end of the 18th century.

40. With the use of metal kilns a metal flue was installed. This one was in the yard of the Sussex Charcoal Burning Company at Charlton, near Singleton, in 1938.

41. A metal flue is set in the core of a small stack of wood enclosed within an iron fence-like frame before being covered with a hood such as those seen on the smoking kilns behind and to the right.

42. When the charcoal is ready the metal cover is hauled by pulley and can be pushed along the scaffolding to another stack of wood. The "cage" within prevents the charcoal falling out of place.

Another style of metal kiln is still in use and can occasionally be seen when timber has been felled. Being portable by lorry, such kilns can be set up where the wood is lying. They may remain in one locality for several weeks before moving to a new site. (Plates 43 and 44). They are built of metal cylinders with a lid and ventilating flues; the construction is clearly set out in the diagram supplied by Messrs. Kings, Fuel Merchants of Edenbridge, in Fig. 8. Messrs. King also gave permission to print from a typescript from an unknown source giving instructions for the use of such a kiln, which reads:

"First choose a level site, with natural fall away for rainwater if this is to be encountered.

Lay out out 4 draught boxes in a rough circle about 7' 6" in diameter, spaced equally apart.

Put the lower ring onto those boxes and fill the small space up with earth, taking it up the side of the ring about 6". You now have the bottom of the ring sealed except for 4 draught boxes. Lay two pieces of wood across the bottom of the kiln opposite one of the draught boxes.

Fill up the kiln with wood packed reasonably tightly but be sure that you lay some pieces across the 2 long pieces already in position so that the space is not blocked. (Later it will be necessary to push a rag soaked in paraffin through the draught box to the centre of the kiln to light up).

Put on the middle and fill up with more wood to slightly above the top.

Put on the lid and if the wood is too high, this does not matter because it will soon drop down.

Get a cleft stick and put the lighted paraffin rag through the draught box to approximately the centre. The wood will catch fire almost immediately because of the draught.

Erect 4 chimneys.

Allow to burn for 17/20 hours. A change in the colour of smoke will tell you when burning is complete.

Take down chimneys, seal hole with earth. Throw earth on to middle section and seal at join. Throw earth on lid and seal on periphery. It is essential that the seal is well done because the smallest amount of air will keep the charcoal hot.

Leave the kiln for 24 hours to cool. Take off the lid and middle, empty charcoal and fill as before.

Kiln holds 2¼ cords of wood, produces about 10/12 cwts charcoal. 1 cord is 128 cubic feet.

A good man and a boy (or woman) can operate 6 kilns, 3 each day to give a rota of about 30 cwts per day.

Charcoal can be produced without kilns by putting up a stack of wood and covering to exclude air. This method I used for several years but it needed more skill and was too slow.''

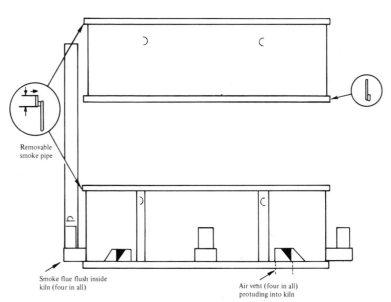

Removable
smoke pipe

Smoke flue flush inside
kiln (four in all)

Air vent (four in all)
protuding into kiln

8.   Diagram of a metal kiln, by courtesy of Messrs. Kings Fuels, Edenbridge,
      Kent.

43. Portable metal kiln on Heyshott Common, 1970.

44. Sections of portable metal kilns, with a kiln smoking in the background.

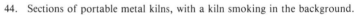

Some users of these kilns seal the joints between the sections with dust — there is a flange in the joint where this can be done — in the early stages of burning: the bottom ventilators will need adjusting during the burn. It has been known, under exceptional conditions, for a metal kiln to burn out its contents. Ordinarily, they are not difficult to control and the burners go home in the evening and do not expect to work a "night shift". Wet weather or snow are troublesome in washing out the seal of dirt but, by comparison with the earth burnt kilns, it is a much easier task to produce and grade charcoal in this manner. The crop is riddled through vibrating mechanically powered sieves — two or more grades being used — and the product tipped down a chute into bags. Burners work throughout the year and travel, often living in a caravan.

The modern continuous retort factory would seem to be the ultimate in efficiency. Here, the plants are worked from a control room and operatives and chemists together make a scientifically pure charcoal. Volatile matter, ash and moisture content, and carbon content, all being kept within very strict control limits. The retorts work semi-automatically, loading several tons of wood at a time, recharging automatically at the top when the processed charcoal is discharged below.

The temperatures are carefully controlled and by-products collected. The charring period even here is irregular — 12 to 24 hours — and after cooling, the char goes into conditioning tanks where it is exposed to the air for about eight days to soak up oxygen and moisture from the air to make it stable once again.

In 1961, two hundred persons were members of the National Association of Charcoal Manufacturers (not including office workers and managerial staff), and it is probable that more charcoal burners, not members of the Association, were actually working. Of the known number, about half were operating portable kilns, the rest being attached to wood distillation plants.[2]

Charcoal burner's camp at the Weald and Downland Open Air Museum.

In contrast, Plate 45 shows a nearly contemporary charcoal burning scene in Morocco: the kilns are easily recognisable but the shelter, in this case, is different.

The final illustration (Plate 46) "Charcoal Burning in the Alps" (c. 1872) has points of interest in the tools used — the long-handled spade in particular corresponds to that described by Miss Hartley, although the exact shape of the rake head is difficult to determine. Here the ladder has been inverted and the ascent of the kiln made easy by sloping planks. "Spiracles" are rising neatly from the steep sides of the kiln, but the hut here is not of turf, it far more nearly corresponds to that shown in the early illustration (Plate 14), which also seems to be in an upland forest setting. It may well be that in places where work was likely to continue for a long time such huts were general and the wood for burning was brought near to them, or they may have been built only in the European mainland. The Open Air Museum at Stubing, near Graz in Austria, has a charcoal burners' hut, also of log construction, amongst its exhibits.

45. Charcoal burning in Morocco, 1957.

46. Charcoal burning in the Alps. Here the curved ladder has been inverted to give support to a plank. The long-handled heart-shaped shovel appears to be "international". It is not clear how the very steep base of the kiln is covered and held together.

USES AND BY-PRODUCTS

The most important use of charcoal in the past was certainly as a fuel but as an ingredient it has also been useful to several metallurgical processes — in brass making, copper smelting and in the "cementation" process in the manufacture of steel. In the glass industry, it was a fuel and an ingredient also. In medieval times, it was used in the manufacture of soap, beech wood charcoal being thought best for this purpose. Its use in gunpowder factories has already been noted but, as early as 1300, there were recipes known in the West for its use in fireworks. As a crayon, it is still used and as a pigment in ink it was already present in ancient times: ink found in Herculaneum was still black after nineteen hundred years. Less romantically, it is also a pigment in shoe blacking.

In Britain, it is used in the manufacture of case-hardening compounds for ferrous and non-ferrous metals. In steel hardening, as a filler for rubber and plastics and in the making of glycerine and electrical batteries. It is a good insulator of temperature and is sometimes used as such. For a time it was burned inside the cavities of charcoal-irons — a halfway stage between the flat-iron and the modern electric one but as a fuel its use in Britain now is confined to barbecues for which it is bought at great price; "The Last Charcoal Burner" supplied it to London's grill rooms.

Second to fuel its importance has been as a filter. The principle by which this takes place is given, so far as is possible, in the Appendix but it has the property of being able to remove toxins and colours from air or water. It has been of service to many industries, such as salt and sugar manufacture as well as in removing undesirable flavour from drinking water and undesirable odour from sewage waste. Its use in gas masks has been touched on. In other ways, it has served in the purification of air — as in hoods over kitchen stoves. How effective it might be as a "digestive" biscuit, whether for human or canine consumption, one cannot say but both have been marketed. It is included in bulb-fibre and charcoal dust is an additive to some fertilisers although not, in this case, serving as a filter.

Its by-products are wood-tar and pyroligneous acid and in modern plants these can be separated. From pyroligneous acid, acetic acid, naptha and some wood oils are obtained. The rayon industry uses acetic acid, which is best obtained from beech wood charcoal. The rayon industry also uses carbon di-sulphide, which is a liquid obtained by passing sulphur vapour over red hot charcoal heated to 800°C. or 900°C. and condensed; for this birch or beech are preferred.

Creosote is a by-product of the wood tar: wood-tar has long been valued for the preservation of wood; in particular, it was required for the treatment of ships' timbers and, with a modification of the old type of kiln, it was possible to collect it in drains. Brick kilns were designed for the purpose but little used. Turpentine and methyl alcohol are also obtained.

APPENDIX

CHARCOAL AS A FILTER: WHY DOES IT WORK?

Why does charcoal have special properties as a filter? In answer to this question the following note has been kindly supplied by Dr. H. Frost, Staff Lecturer in Physical Sciences at the University of London, who nevertheless prefaces his remarks by saying: "I am not sure that the mechanism whereby charcoal absorbs traces of undesired substances is fully understood".

. . . .

The production of charcoal is by controlled burning with a restricted air supply: the air initially present in-between the sticks and in the pores of the wood, plus as much air as the charcoal burner allows to enter through holes at the bottom.

Wood consists of cellulose — a compound of carbon, hydrogen and oxygen. (Also a few other gases and liquids from the sap). The hydrogen and oxygen are always present in the ratio of two atoms of hydrogen to one of oxygen as in water and they are expelled as water in the burning of the wood. Given an initial start by raising the temperature locally (lighting the fire), this process begins and the carbon combines with oxygen to give carbon dioxide, giving out heat in the process (i.e. the process is exothermic). This heat keeps the process going and if there is plenty of air, the process goes to completion. The burner allows enough air to burn enough of the carbon to generate enough heat to drive off all the water. If he is too generous with air, his yield of charcoal is reduced. If he is too mean with air, he produces too much scorched wood not properly converted to charcoal.

The process, whereby charcoal absorbs traces of undesired substances is technically called "adsorption" and is analogous to the wetting of surfaces by water. If you pass water through tubes, a surface film is retained. If the tube is greasy, no water is retained.

Charcoal is similarly selective, adsorbing some substances in preference to others. It selectively adsorbs gases, liquids or substances in solution in liquids. It will, for example, adsorb 170 parts by volume of ammonia, but only 18 parts of oxygen and 15 parts of nitrogen, so air contaminated by ammonia will be largely cleaned by passing through charcoal. Similarly, it will improve air contaminated with chlorine as in gas masks.

Gas masks contain "activated charcoal", which has been heated in the absence of air to about 900°C. (red heat). The effect is to drive off material obstructing some of the pores of ordinary charcoal.

The surface area offered by charcoal may be as much as two thousand square metres per gram. The problem is to remove minute traces (less than one part per million) of substances to which human beings are very sensitive. We can taste, smell or be poisoned by quite small numbers of molecules of some substances. These substances comprise large molecules (dozens, hundreds, or even thousands of atoms) carried in solution by a substance comprising small molecules (e.g. water molecules have three atoms only: H-O-H).

The large surface area is critical because the undesired molecules have to come in contact with the carbon. This is highly probable if the vehicle (e.g. water), passes through the pores of the charcoal in layers only a few molecules thick and highly unlikely if the carbon were a solid chunk with most of its carbon atoms inaccessible in the interior of the lump. In charcoal the carbon atoms are linked together in planes one atom thick by fairly strong bonds and the planes are linked together by weaker bonds. (This is why graphite acts as a lubricant — the planes slide over each other when movement occurs). These weak bonds are quite easily broken and quite easily unite with similar weak bonds on the outside of the large molecules. (This is the point where the chemists are reluctant to go into detail). The "bonds" are interactions between electrons orbiting around atoms: a weak bond means that an electron is not heavily committed to interaction with a particular nearby electron and is ready to interact with another.

Clearly there is a limit to the process. You cannot use carbon to remove large quantities of material. Gas masks which have come in contact with gas need to have the charcoal replaced — it can be reactivated by intense reheating.

It is not known exactly at what time charcoal came into service as a purifying agent. In 1785, Johann Tobias Lowitz, then teaching at the Imperial Pharmacy at St. Petersburg, published a paper dealing with the adsorption of colouring matter from tartaric acid on wood charcoal. He followed up this with several other memoirs on the subject, including the use of charcoal with brandy and drinking water.

INTRODUCTION
Notes

1. Chambers Encyclopaedia.
2. Sussex Archaeological Collections. Vol. 29, pp. 167-180.
3. C. J. Bond. Unpublished papers, sources given as follows:
   (a) Forest Charters, "Stubbs Select Charters".
   (b) J. Birrel, "Peasant Craftsmen in the Medieval Forest", Agricultural History Review. Vol. 17. 1969.
   (c) From a note by Wickham Steed held in Oxfordshire County Museum.
   (d) Cox. Royal Forests of England.
   (e) Calendar of Close Rolls, 1288-96.
4. Ernest Straker. "Wealden Iron".
5. Straker, *op. cit.*
6. W. Pennington. History of British Vegetation.
7. Miles Hadfield. "Landscape with Trees".
8. From the Machell of Pennybridge family records at the Lancashire Record Office.

THE CHARCOAL-BURNING LIFE
Notes

1. Edward Freeman, "The Reign of Wm. Rufus & the Accession of Henry I". Vol. 2. (1882).
2. C. J. Bond. Papers as yet unpublished.
3. By permission of the County Archivist for Hampshire. Crown copyright.
4. With the permission of the County Archivist for Essex. Crown copyright.
5. With the permission of the County Archivist for Essex. Crown copyright.
6. With the permission of the County Archivist for W. Sussex. Crown copyright.
7. With the permission of the County Archivist for Kent. Crown copyright.
8. With the permission of the County Archivist for Kent. Crown copyright.
9. With the permission of the County Archivist for Kent. Crown copyright.
10. By permission of the County Records Officer for E. Sussex. Transcriptions of Crown copyright records appear by permission of the Controller of H.M. Stationery Office.
11. Diocesan Records Office, Lichfield.
12. John West, "Village Records".
13. E. Sussex Records Office.
14. J. Corbet Anderson. "Ancient description concerning the Parish of Croydon". 1882.
15. John Bennington (?). "A few words on Collyers Water". 1852
16. W. R. Butterfield. Sussex County Magazine. Sept. 1938.
17. J. S. P. Agg Large, "Lonely Men of the Forest". Hampshire Magazine. Oct. 1967.
18. J. G. Jenkins. "Traditional Country Crafts".
19. N. A. J. Wilde. "Charcoal Burning in Wyre Forest". Quarterly Journal of Forestry. Oct. 1974.
20. C. J. Bond. Unpublished papers.
21. M. A. J. Wilde, *op. cit.*
22. J. G. Jenkins, *op. cit.*

* John Saddler of Brightling, p. 22.

HUT BUILDING
Notes

1. James Walton. "Gwerin" was a journal of folk life published by Messrs. Blackwell of Oxford.
2. Sussex County Magazine. Sept. 1938.
3. Quarterly Journal of Forestry. Oct. 1974.
4. Quoted by Mr. Walton in "Gwerin".
5. Diagram showing details of the roof-tree construction are given in Mr. Walton's "Gwerin" article and in "Industrial Archaeology of the Lake Counties" by M. Davies Shiel and J. D. Marshall.

THE CHARCOAL KILN
Notes

1. "Microcosm of Early Trades & Industries". Pyne. Abbreviated edition published by the Luton Museum.
2. "Sweden". Published by Cassell & Co. Ltd.
3. Miles Hadfield. "Landscape with Trees".
4. J. Bowden. "The Last Charcoal Burner". Sussex County Magazine. 1939.
5. Margaret Baker. "Discovering the Folklore of Plants".
6. N. A. J. Wild, *op. cit.*
7. Dorothy Hartley. "Made in England".
8. J. D. Marshall & M. Davies Shiel. "The Lake District at Work, Past and Present".
9. W. R. Butterfield, *op. cit.*
10. Surtees Soc. Vol. 54, p. 247, "Diary of John Hobson of Dodsworth Green, Nr. Barnsley".

THE YIELD AND ITS VALUE
Notes

1. From the "Machell of Pennybridge" family records at the Lancashire Records Office.
2. H. L. Edlin. "Woodland Crafts in Britain".
3. E. Straker. "Wealden Iron".
4. From the "Machell of Pennybridge" family records at the Lancashire Records Office.
5. Forest Records. The Manufacture of Wood Charcoal in Great Britain. H.M.S.O.
6. Kings Fuels, Edenbridge, Kent.

NEW TIMES, NEW METHODS
Notes

1. Forest Records. "The Manufacture of Wood Charcoal in Great Britain". H.M.S.O.
2. Forest Records, *op. cit.*

BIBLIOGRAPHY

In addition to the various magazine articles and pamphlets listed in the textual footnotes, the following books have sections dealing with charcoal burning:

Arnold, J. "The Shell Book of Country Crafts".
Edlin, H. L. "Woodland Crafts in Britain".
Hartley, D. "Made in England".
Jenkins, J. G. "Traditional Country Crafts".
Marshall, J. D. & Davies-Shiel, M. "The Lake District at Work, Past and Present".
Marshall, J. D. & Davies-Shiel, M. "The Industrial Archaeology of the Lakes Counties".
Mitchell, P. "The Pegasus Book of Country Crafts".
Woods, K. S. "Rural Crafts in England".
Wymer, N. "English Country Crafts".

On burning with a metal kiln: Mannings, J. E. "Country Crafts Today".

A drawing and explanatory note is found in "A Microcosm of Early Trades and Industries". Pyne. Abridged edn. Luton Museum publications.

An interesting chapter, "Fuel", is found in the extremely interesting "Wealden Iron", by Ernest Straker — on which the present writer has leaned heavily for information.

The filming of the Ickenthwaite burn was by Countrywide Films Ltd. That of the Statterthwaite burn was by Mr. S. Hanna of Brun Educational Films Ltd.

Film strip, "Charcoal Burners' Craft", 20 frame colour slides, taken at Singleton Museum. Hugh Baddeley Productions, 77 Moffats Lane, Brookmans Park, Hatfield, Herts. (993-63-348).